pregnancy
food

pregnancy food

sophie braimbridge
jenny copeland SRD

photography by
deirdre rooney

MURDOCH
B O O K S

contents

eating well in pregnancy

Making sure you eat a healthy diet is one of the most important things you can do for you and your baby. For nine whole months your body goes through the most amazing changes to protect and nourish your baby. The food that you eat now not only helps your baby grow and develop but shapes your own body too, keeping you fit and well and helping you avoid or overcome the common ailments that can occur. A healthy diet will also give you the energy and nutrients you need for birth and breastfeeding.

Your body has different nutritional requirements during each of the three distinct stages – or trimesters – of pregnancy. In the pages that follow you will find plenty of expert advice about how your body changes during pregnancy and healthy eating habits that will nourish you and your growing baby. You'll also find a selection of easy and delicious recipes, packed full of nutritious ingredients to suit your body's needs at the various stages of pregnancy.

Eat well now and you will not only nourish your growing baby but also reap the rewards long after the birth.

learning to eat well

Not only is it vital to eat a healthy, balanced diet during all stages of your pregnancy, it's also essential that you eat well before you conceive, so that your body can supply your rapidly developing baby with all the nutritional elements needed to fuel growth. However, you may only need to make small changes to improve your diet, and there's no need to eat for two. Every pregnant woman will start off with different nutritional needs, depending on her health and body's nutrient stores, and her needs will change as pregnancy progresses. The most important thing to remember is to regularly eat a variety of healthy foods. There are, however, some foods that you should try to avoid:

* Eating too many 'junk' foods may prevent you from getting all the nutrients that you need.
* Eating fatty foods may mean you take in a lot of calories very quickly, as their energy content is extremely concentrated.

By eating a good variety and balance of foods, maintaining some sort of regular, gentle activity and getting plenty of rest and relaxation (and not smoking or drinking), you can give yourself and your developing baby the best chance of a healthy body and life.

The food you eat now provides the nutrients (or building blocks) to help your body function properly. In order for you to get all of the essential nutrients – carbohydrates, proteins, fats, vitamins and minerals – you need to focus on getting the right balance of food groups in your diet.

CARBOHYDRATE-RICH FOODS

Carbohydrates are a group of nutrients that includes sugars, starches and fibre (or roughage). All carbohydrates are made up of sugar units and are broken down by digestion into these sugars, which are carried in the blood to provide the body with the energy for vital bodily processes including growth, activity and pregnancy.

Some types of carbohydrate-rich foods are more slowly digested than others, causing a slower, more gradual release of energy into your body. Examples include oats (porridge or muesli), basmati rice, pasta, milk products, some breakfast cereals, beans, chickpeas and lentils, heavy fruit breads and wholesome breads containing wholegrains, such as rye bread. Meals based on these foods help prevent your blood sugar level from rising too high, which is particularly important if you are diagnosed with gestational diabetes. However, if you don't have a problem with high blood sugar levels, you can still enjoy all other types of healthy carbohydrate-rich foods that suit your taste preferences and appetite. You may find that you can only eat relatively small meals during the later stages of your pregnancy, but it is important that you focus on a regular intake of grains and cereal products to supply you with the fibre, energy and B-group vitamins you need. Look for breakfast cereals that have extra vitamins and minerals added into them.

Because carbohydrates are packed with energy, they should make up at least half of your diet. On average most women need between 1800–2000 kcal (or 8.10 MJ) per day depending on their current activity and health status, with an extra 300 kcal a day during the last few months of pregnancy.

PROTEIN-RICH FOODS

Meat and fish, as well as their vegetarian alternatives, contain protein – essential amino acids, which are the building blocks needed to repair and maintain all body cells as well as to grow the new ones needed in pregnancy. They are essential for the extra blood production and building up the immune system to combat infection at this important time.

Proteins should normally make up 10–15 percent of a normal diet, with an extra 6g (¼oz) per day in pregnancy.

FRUIT, VEGETABLES AND DAIRY FOODS

These foods contain many of the essential vitamins and minerals that are needed to maintain the health and well being of you and your baby.

VITAMINS – There are two types of vitamins: water-soluble (C and B complex) and fat-soluble (A, D, E and K). The water-soluble vitamins cannot be stored in the body and may be lost from foods during cooking, so a regular supply is essential. If you eat a balanced diet that includes a good variety of fruit and vegetables, you should get plenty of vitamins and minerals, so it should not be necessary to take supplements unless you are advised to by a medical practitioner. Always check with your doctor, midwife or pharmacist before taking any over-the-counter supplements during pregnancy.

∗ **Vitamin A** This is needed for the formation of healthy eyes and skin early on in pregnancy and is also an important antioxidant, helping to protect the body against many diseases. A daily intake of 600 mcg (750 mcg in Australia) is recommended, while pregnant women should take in an extra 100 mcg. An excessive intake from supplements or liver products should be avoided as these may be harmful to a developing baby.

There are two forms of vitamin A – retinol (found in animal foods such as liver) and beta-carotene (in plant foods such as carrots). Because of the high amounts of retinol given to animals in their feeds, animal livers can contain dangerously high amounts of vitamin A. An excessive intake of vitamin A can produce a number of toxic side effects such as hair loss, headaches and liver and bone damage. In pregnancy an excess is thought to increase the risk of miscarriage and birth defects.

* **The B vitamins** This group of vitamins work together and include B1 (thiamine), B2 (riboflavin), B3 (nicotinic acid), folate (folic acid), B6 (pyridoxine), B12 (cobalamin) and biotin. They are needed for the formation of healthy immune and nervous systems and for the production of red blood cells and energy.

* **Folate** Extra folate is vital during pregnancy for the formation of new cells and tissues in the mother and baby. It is therefore recommended that women take 400mcg of folate each day in the three months prior to conception and for the first three months of pregnancy. A folic acid supplement is usually necessary because it may be difficult to get enough from your diet alone. Take it with other B vitamin-rich foods for maximum effect.

Folate is needed to reduce the risk of your baby developing spina bifida and other serious defects early on in pregnancy, when the spine is forming. It is also needed for the formation of red blood cells and the normal growth of the baby's brain.

* **Vitamin C** This vitamin is vital for the production of collagen – a protein needed for healthy skin, bone, gums and teeth, and for an efficient immune system. Vitamin C also helps enhance the absorption of iron in your diet. The normal recommended daily amount is 40mg, with an extra 10mg a day recommended for pregnant women.

* **Vitamin D** This vitamin is needed for the absorption of the mineral calcium and so is essential for the development of your baby's bones and teeth. It is mainly made in your skin after it is exposed to sunlight.

* **Vitamin E** This is needed for healthy cell and tissue formation early on in pregnancy and also for the development of healthy lungs. Currently there are no recommended intakes during pregnancy but an estimated safe intake for women of childbearing age is around 7mg a day. Breastfeeding women need another 2.5mg of vitamin E each day.

MINERALS – We need a wide range of minerals in the right amounts for many important body functions, including the formation and maintenance of strong bones, teeth, a healthy immune system, growth and for many vitamins to function. Like vitamins, some are only needed in very small amounts (trace elements). So by eating a varied and balanced diet you should get the required amounts. The important ones include:

* **Iron** This mineral is needed for healthy blood and muscles. Your baby will get all the iron needed from your blood supply, which means that your body will have to increase the amount it makes. For most

women the recommended average daily amount is 14.8 mg and it has been estimated that an extra 2.6mg a day is needed during pregnancy.

* **Zinc** This is essential for healthy reproduction and the normal growth and development of your baby. The requirement for zinc is increased from 12 mg a day in non-pregnant women to 15–16mg a day when you are pregnant.

* **Calcium** This mineral is vital for bone formation. During the last trimester of pregnancy, an adequate calcium intake is essential as the baby's teeth and skeleton are forming rapidly. Pregnant women naturally become more efficient at absorbing calcium in foods, so the recommended daily intake is not increased above normal (700mg a day).

* **Potassium** This is needed for healthy cell, muscle, heart and nerve function and to help control blood pressure. The daily requirement for potassium is not increased above the normal level (3500mg a day) and this should easily be met if you are consuming 4–5 portions of fruit and vegetables each day.

* **Phosphorus** This is needed for bone and teeth formation, energy production and for the absorption of many nutrients. The daily requirement is about 550 mg, which is sufficient for pregnancy too.

* **Magnesium** This is essential for the formation of healthy nerves, muscles, bones and teeth. It may help prevent muscle cramps and morning sickness and 270 mg are required each day.

* **Manganese** This is needed for the body's antioxidant defence systems, for normal fat and carbohydrate metabolism and for brain function (1.4mg a day).

* **Selenium** This is an antioxidant mineral that protects cells from damage and is needed for reproduction (it is particularly useful before conception). 60 mcg a day is needed.

(See pages 28–42 for examples of food containing these minerals.)

WATER
We need a daily intake of at least 2.5 litres (4½ pints) of fluid, of which at least 1.8 litres (3¼ pints) should be water – that's about eight glasses a day. By the middle of your pregnancy you should be drinking an extra 6–8 glasses a day. Avoid dehydrating drinks such as tea and coffee – water and diluted fruit juices are better.

FATS
The two main types of fat are saturated fat and unsaturated fat (which includes polyunsaturated fats and monounsaturated fats). Pregnant women don't need any more fat than normal, but focus on eating a healthy balance of different fats, including the essential omega-3 fats. Keep your intake of saturated fat to a minimum, and eat a variety of nuts and seeds, eggs and oily fish.

A BALANCED DIET

FOOD GROUP	AN AVERAGE PORTION IS
Starchy foods like bread, potatoes and cereals *At least six portions needed each day*	* 1 slice of bread or toast * A small roll or bun * 2 small potatoes or an average jacket potato * 30g (2 heaped tbsp) of cooked rice * 45g (3 heaped tbsp) of cooked pasta * A bowl of cereal, muesli or porridge
Fruit and vegetables *At least five portions needed each day*	* 15g (1 heaped tbsp) of cooked vegetables * A side salad * 1 piece of fresh fruit * A bowl of strawberries or fruit salad * A small glass of fruit juice
Milk and dairy products or alternatives *Three portions needed each day*	* A medium glass of milk * A small carton of yoghurt * A carton of cottage cheese * 25–50g (1–2oz) cheese – a small square * A medium carton of fromage frais
Protein-rich foods like meat, fish, eggs and vegetarian alternatives *Two portions needed each day*	* 2 eggs * 75–100g (3–4oz) lean meat: pork, ham, lamb, chicken or fish: oily or white * 75g (5 tbsp) of baked beans * 60g (4 tbsp) of cooked lentils, red kidney beans or chickpeas * 30g (2 tbsp) of nuts * 100g (2–4oz) Quorn, soya mince or textured vegetable protein
Essential fats *One to two portions needed each day*	* 5g (1 tsp) of vegetable oil margarine or 10g (2 tsp) of low fat spread * 100g (4oz) portion of oily fish * 15g (1 tbsp) of seeds or nuts * 5–10g (1–2 tsp) of olive or linseed oil
Water/fluids *8–10 glasses a day*	* 1 large glass or beaker

pre-conceptual nutritional needs

As soon as you have decided that you wish to have a baby, a healthy diet and lifestyle should become a top priority. Start at least three months before trying to conceive, to give your body the chance to stock up on essential vitamins such as folic acid, as well as clear out any toxins like caffeine.

TAKING FOLIC ACID

A shortage of the B vitamin folic acid/folate at a critical point in a baby's body formation can, if combined with a genetic tendency, cause the severe birth defect spina bifida. This is why it is advisable for women who want to start a family to take 400 mcg folic acid supplement each day three months before and after conception in conjunction with eating folate-rich foods.

SUBSTANCES TO AVOID

The latest scientific evidence suggests that to have the best chance of conceiving a healthy baby you should cut down on caffeinated drinks and avoid alcohol.

ALCOHOL – An excessive amount drunk by either partner may hinder you from conceiving and also lower the levels of folic acid in your body. (It can also lower the absorption of B vitamins and important minerals such as zinc). Pregnant women (or those wishing to conceive) should limit their intake to one

unit a day, which is a glass of wine, half a pint of beer or a single measure of a spirit. You may wish to give up alcohol altogether, which is what experts suggest.

CAFFEINATED DRINKS – Tea, coffee, hot chocolate and some soft fizzy drinks such as cola provide a short energy boost – few offer vitamins and minerals – and can also stop you from consuming healthier foods and drinks. Drinking more than 4–5 caffeinated drinks a day during pregnancy has been associated with a small risk of low birth weights and miscarriage. Try to cut down to one or two caffeinated drinks a day or stop altogether.

There are many delicious alternatives. Try an energy-boosting homemade fruit shake in the morning and herbal, fruit or ginger tea bags at work. Drink elderflower cordial instead of canned drinks.

the first trimester – weeks 1–12

The beginning of your pregnancy, from the moment your baby is conceived until it begins to show, is when the most rapid changes are occurring. These changes require specific nutrients at certain times.

From the moment that you become pregnant your body and vital organs become involved in the growth and nourishment of your baby. In particular your heart, lungs, bones, blood vessels, blood, breasts, digestive system, kidneys, ligaments, skin and, of course, hormonal system will all experience changes.

During your pregnancy you can expect to gain 11–15kg (25–35lb) as you and your baby increase in size. Your uterus, which starts off the size and shape of a small 60g (2oz) pear, will end up larger than a watermelon and weigh as much as 1kg (2lb). New blood vessels and muscle fibres grow to form the placenta – your

baby's lifeline – and you make an extra 1.25 litres (2¼ pints) of blood. To do this your body has to make more blood cells. Your kidneys also grow to cope with the waste products resulting from your baby's metabolism. By the end of your pregnancy you'll also be carrying up to 6 litres (10½ pints) more fluid. So it's not surprising your heart works harder, pumping out 7 litres (12 pints) of blood per minute instead of its usual 5 litres (8½ pints).

Changes also happen in your gastro-intestinal tract, which slows down in order for you to absorb food more efficiently, to get maximum energy and nutrients from it. With all these rapid changes you may feel tired, nauseous and have tender breasts.

YOUR BABY'S DEVELOPMENT

By four weeks after conception, the fertilized egg will have been implanted in the lining of your uterus, which makes you biologically pregnant and the rapid growth of new life will have begun. Just a week or two later your baby's major organs are already beginning to form and the heart will begin beating. The spinal cord forms and the nervous system starts to send messages to enable your baby's first movements. During the next couple of weeks the umbilical cord will have formed and will transport nutrients directly from your own bloodstream into your baby's.

* By week 10 all the major structures of your baby's internal organs have been formed, including the heart, brain, lungs, kidney, liver, gut and sex organs. A face with eyes, mouth and tongue is also forming. Your baby will be about 22mm (almost 1in) long from head to bottom.

YOUR CHANGING BODY

One of the first things that you may notice early on in your pregnancy is that you feel increasingly tired. This is a normal result of all the changes taking place in your body.

* By week 6 the levels of hormones such as progesterone and oestrogen are rapidly increasing and as a result you may begin to feel sick or go off certain foods. You may notice breast changes too as they start to get bigger and more sensitive.

EATING TIPS

It is important to continue taking the folic acid supplements you began before you conceived. Folic acid is essential for your baby's spinal cord and nerves, so eat folate-rich foods such as broccoli and green leafy vegetables too. Also avoid alcohol and 'at risk foods' as your baby will be sensitive to germs and toxins.

You should also regularly eat plenty of nutritious carbohydrate-rich foods, such as bread, pasta and breakfast cereals, in order to combat your tiredness and ensure a constant supply of important nutrients. This is also a good time to regularly eat oily fish, which contains essential fats needed for the formation of your baby's brain.

If you suffer from morning sickness, yoghurt- or milk-based smoothies may be soothing. They also boost your calcium and vitamin D intakes, needed for the baby's skeleton to form. Eating small regular meals may keep nausea at bay.

* By week 8–10 you will need extra iron as your placenta is forming. Ensure you are eating a balanced diet and pay close attention to your intake of iron-rich foods (see pages 28–42 for more information).

YOU AND YOUR BABY'S NUTRITIONAL NEEDS

* Your baby's muscles, blood and other tissues contain iron, protein, minerals, vitamins and other essential nutrients that are supplied through your bloodstream directly from the food that you have eaten. Iron is a vital part of haemoglobin, the building block of red blood cells that enables blood to carry oxygen to every part of the body. At this time you need to produce around one third more blood than usual, plus the baby must create its own supply.

* Your placenta transfers nutrients from you to your baby continuously. If your dietary intake of any of them is low – especially iron – then your baby will obtain them from your own incoming supply, possibly using it up. It is therefore vital that you try to eat more healthy nutrients.

the second trimester – weeks 13–27

You will begin to 'show off' your growing baby as your bump gets bigger. As the placenta takes over, your hormones should begin to settle, so you'll feel less tired and sick. Indeed, for most women, the second trimester is the easiest. However, water retention, backaches and lower stomach aches can occur.

YOUR BABY'S DEVELOPMENT

Your baby is still growing rapidly and the body will become more in proportion with the head. During this phase, your baby will gain 1kg in weight (2.2lb), and be about 30cm (1ft) from head to bottom.

By now you may feel the first of many of your baby's movements.

* By week 16 the fingers, nose and toes are fully formed. Your baby has the same number of nerve cells as you and the bones are beginning to harden.

* By week 21 the glands are producing vernix caseosa, which coats the skin to protect it from the amniotic fluid that surrounds your baby.

During this time your baby will be beginning to react to touch, and the taste buds and teeth are also forming. The lungs and digestive system are functioning, but are still very immature.

* By week 27 your baby will be moving around vigorously. He or she can also swallow small amounts of amniotic fluid, which may cause hiccups!

YOUR CHANGING BODY

The most noticeable change to your body during these weeks will be its size as your belly and breasts continue to grow. You should expect to gain 0.5 kg (1 lb) a week due to your growing baby and your increasing blood supply, amniotic fluid, placenta and a small amount of fat. Your appetite should be increasing too and any morning sickness that you've suffered from should ease.

You may experience a heightened sense of taste and smell along with food cravings, which can affect your intake, causing you to avoid certain foods and crave others. This is usually harmless, as long as you're not avoiding entire food groups or craving non-edible items. It can be helpful too, as it often prevents mothers from ingesting bitter, potentially harmful substances. Beware of salt

cravings – although you don't need to avoid salt altogether, you shouldn't eat too much, especially if you have high blood pressure or are prone to water retention.

* By week 20 (halfway) you'll become increasingly aware of the compression of your stomach by your growing baby and may begin to experience heartburn. You may be hungry, yet get full rapidly.

EATING TIPS

As your baby is growing fast it is important to eat regularly to keep a constant supply of energy and nutrients. You still need to eat folate-rich foods, folate-fortified cereals and omega-3 fats from oily fish, seeds, oils and nuts in your diet to aid the growth of your baby's eyes, nerves and brain. Fruit and vegetables, rich in beta-carotene, will help protect the developing body cells from getting damaged.

You should also make sure that you are including at least two portions of protein-rich foods a day, as your growing baby needs the amino acids provided by milk, fish, eggs, beans and pulses.

Certain herbs, including cohosh, rue, golden seal, feverfew, penny royal, comfrey, chamomile, tansy and raspberry tea, can have severe laxative effects or cause the uterus to contract, so should be avoided at this time. Always use reputable brands of herbal teas and check the labels carefully. An excess of vitamin A from supplements and liver products should also be avoided (see page 9).

Because of the increase in your blood volume, the need to make more amniotic fluid and the necessity of flushing out the extra waste products, you will need to drink more water. Make sure you drink at least 6–8 glasses of extra fluids a day in the form of water or diluted fruit juices – avoid caffeinated drinks (see page 13).

As a result of the compression of your stomach you should try to eat six nutritious small meals a days. Although you may have cravings, try not to give in to the temptation of eating junk food. In order to avoid or alleviate heartburn, steer clear of rich fatty foods. Eat plain lean meats and fish, salads and pasta dishes. Also choose foods that are nutrient-dense such as eggs, beans and nuts. Starchy foods such as toast, raisin bread and bananas are nutritious as snacks.

the third trimester – weeks 28-40

You will feel, and probably see, your baby move every day. This is also the most likely time that you will experience heartburn, constipation and discomfort. Your baby and your body will be starting to get ready for labour and the imminent birth, which normally happens anytime from week 38–42, although rarely on the due date.

YOUR BABY'S DEVELOPMENT

By week 30, your baby's features are well developed and by week 34 the body is perfectly formed and in proportion.

Your baby's eyes are able to open and shut now, the eyelashes and eyebrows are formed and the eye colour is slate grey. Your baby may have quite a lot of hair by now. The lungs are maturing fast so the baby can take its first breath after birth, while the brain surface is beginning to develop grooves. Even inside the womb

your baby will be sensitive to what's going on around it and will be able to recognize your voice.

During this time the baby's head usually engages into the mother's pelvic cavity in preparation for birth. The time when the baby turns its head around from being under your chest to down towards the birth canal can vary greatly, from four weeks to just before the delivery (or sometimes not at all).

* **By week 36** the vernix caseosa has virtually disappeared, your baby's fingernails have grown to reach the end of the fingers and the eyes have become blue. The face will now be smooth and your baby will put on about eight per cent of its total weight in fat at this time.

* **By week 36** your baby will be gaining about 14g (½oz) of fat a day in order to cope with the lower temperatures after birth and will be nearing its birth size.

YOUR CHANGING BODY

Your weight will still be increasing gradually as your baby becomes fully grown. Your abdomen will be huge, which will make you more likely to experience some of the common ailments, particularly digestive problems.

You may be feeling tired due to the extra weight that you are carrying and you may find it more difficult to move around. The increase in blood volume may cause your iron count to go down.

EATING TIPS

Heartburn is a common problem in the third trimester (see page 24). It is due to pregnancy hormones relaxing the gastro-intestinal tract and the pressure exerted by the baby. Eating small meals regularly throughout the day, rather than three large meals, can reduce or prevent heartburn. Low-fat foods such as cereal products, fruit, vegetables, lean meats and low-fat dairy products are more easily digested than fatty foods and are less likely to cause heartburn. Avoiding caffeine can also help.

During the third trimester you should ensure that you eat plenty of iron-rich foods such as meat and vegetable alternatives, both for your own health and because your baby needs it now and in the first few months after the birth if you are breastfeeding.

As you may not feel like cooking so much in the later stages of your pregnancy, have a supply of nutritious high-energy snacks to hand such as bananas, dried fruit and nuts, sandwiches and smoothies (see pages 48–9 in the Vital Foods section for further ideas). If you have prepared and frozen some meals in advance, then make sure they are piping hot when you reheat them so that you can avoid bacterial contaminations that may harm you or your baby (see pages 20–1).

You may experience problems sleeping due to the extra weight you are carrying around. If so, try including some protein-rich foods like milky drinks, chicken sandwiches and cereals with milk an hour or so before going to bed, as they may help induce sleep.

FOODS FOR LABOUR

* Energy-releasing foods during labour can help prevent tiredness and dehydration and give you the energy needed to sustain labour. Vitamin K, which is found in broccoli, spinach, beans, watercress, avocados, cabbage and cauliflower, is needed for blood clotting, to prevent haemorrhaging and help healing after the birth. Zinc is also important to encourage hormone production and healing after birth. Here are some tips for before and during the delivery.

* Eat plenty of carbohydrate-rich foods before the birth to build up your energy reserves – e.g. starchy vegetables, pulses, pasta, wholegrains, jacket potatoes, toast, rice salads and cereals.

* Pack plenty of snack foods in your labour bag – including non-fizzy fluids (such as bottled still mineral water), dried fruit and nut mixtures, unsalted potato snacks, cereal, yoghurt and fruit and muesli snack bars.

* Eat small, frequent carbohydrate-rich snacks during the birth to sustain your blood sugar levels – such as bananas, cereal bars, sandwiches, fruit and bread – or sip on sports drinks.

food safety in pregnancy

Your placenta keeps most but not all germs away from your baby. There are a few food-related germs that could harm your baby's health as well as your own so it is important to be extra vigilant about hygiene when preparing food.

LISTERIOSIS

This illness is caused by the listeria bacteria and only becomes a problem if the infection passes from a pregnant woman to her unborn baby. Symptoms include a mild flu-like attack with aches and pains, a raised temperature and a sore throat. If the infection passes to the baby, there is a chance it may cause miscarriage, premature labour or serious illness in the newborn baby. It can be diagnosed by a blood or urine test and prompt antibiotic treatment will help reduce the harm to the baby. It is a very rare illness today.

Listeria bacteria are found in the soil and on vegetation and can sometimes contaminate certain foods. You can only catch listeria if you eat a food containing the germ. Listeria continues to grow slowly inside a fridge so always wash salads and raw foods well and only eat well cooked or thoroughly reheated food.

SALMONELLA

This bacteria is a common cause of food poisoning. It can cause severe vomiting, diarrhoea, a high temperature and dehydration. Although your baby is not likely to be directly harmed, you can become very unwell. The bacteria can usually be traced back to poultry products, particularly hen's eggs and chicken meat. It thrives in food that hasn't been sufficiently heated to kill the bacteria.

TOXOPLASMOSIS

This is an illness caused by a tiny parasite called *Toxoplasma gondii*, found in cat faeces. It is usually harmless in adults but can pass from a mother to her unborn baby. Often there are no symptoms or it may cause mild, flu-like symptoms. The harm caused to the baby will depend on the stage of the pregnancy. The most dangerous time is the first half of pregnancy, when the baby's body is developing. You will be immune to it if you've been in previous contact with it, which then gives your baby immunity. It can be found in raw, undercooked and cured meat and occasionally goat's milk, and any food that has been in contact with contaminated soil or animals, particularly cats. It can be diagnosed with a blood test and drugs given can reduce the risk to the baby.

PEANUT ALLERGY ALERT

* If you or your immediate family suffer from asthma, eczema, hay fever or other allergies, then avoid peanuts as they can cause a dangerous allergic reaction in some children.

FOODS TO AVOID	REASON	SAFE ALTERNATIVES
MEAT – raw or undercooked meats and poultry	May contain toxoplasma or salmonella	Well cooked meat and chicken
LIVER and products containing liver such as pâtés and sausage	Contains high levels of retinol (the animal form of vitamin A)	Vegetable pâté, meat pastes in jars, pasteurized pâté – except liver pâté
EGGS – raw or undercooked eggs or foods likely to contain them * Homemade sorbet, mousse, meringue and ice cream * Homemade mayonnaise	May contain salmonella	* Eggs cooked until both yolk and egg are solid * Commercially produced mayonnaise in jars and other products made using pasteurized eggs
MILK – untreated, green top milk from cows, sheep or goats	Because of the risk of brucellosis, listeria and toxoplasmosis	Pasteurized, sterilized or ultra-heat-treated (UHT) milk
CHEESE * Soft, ripened cheese * Blue-veined cheese * Unpasteurized cheese * Cheese made from goat's or sheep's milk	May contain listeria	* Hard cheeses such as cheddar * Soft, processed cheeses * Mozzarella, cottage cheese and other pasteurized cheeses
FRUIT AND VEGETABLES * Unwashed fruit, vegetables and salad	May contain listeria or the toxoplasmosis parasite	Well washed raw vegetables
COOKED- CHILLED READY MEALS * Unheated cooked-chilled meals and pre-cooked and chilled poultry foods not reheated safely	May contain listeria	Only cooked-chilled convenience meals and ready-to-eat poultry that has been thoroughly reheated.
SHELLFISH * Raw or undercooked	Risk of bacteria that may cause food poisoning	Cooked shellfish

alleviating common ailments

Although most women remain healthy and well throughout their pregnancy, few are lucky enough to escape all of the minor ailments that can cause concern or discomfort. Some of the more common problems that can be alleviated by simple changes or additions to your diet are included here. However, if your symptoms persist or you are concerned about them consult your midwife or doctor.

ANAEMIA

Iron deficiency anaemia is common during pregnancy because many women start their pregnancy with relatively low iron stores. Iron requirements are high during this time, because iron is needed for the production of haemoglobin and other essential iron-containing proteins in the mother's and baby's bodies. If your haemoglobin levels are low, you probably have an iron deficiency and your body tissues won't be getting enough oxygen. Oxygen is needed to release energy from your body's stores of fats and sugars. (In addition to iron, vitamin B12 and folic acid are also needed by the body for healthy blood formation.)

During pregnancy your body needs to produce much more blood, consisting of both red blood cells and plasma (the liquid component of blood). This means that your blood can become more dilute. Therefore, your haemoglobin levels may be slightly lower than usual. If you are expecting twins or triplets, have had a baby within the last two years, are vegetarian, have been dieting recently or used to have heavy periods, then your iron stores can be low. See your doctor for advice about your iron status and to check whether you need a supplement.

Symptoms of depleted iron stores include tiredness, paleness, shortness of breath, dizziness and depression. It can also lower your ability to cope with infection, which will make you feel generally unwell and washed out. A simple blood test carried out early on in pregnancy and in the middle months will detect anaemia. If the tests show that you are definitely anaemic, you will probably be prescribed iron tablets. Iron tablets can sometimes cause constipation or stomach pains. If they do, ask your doctor for an alternative.

* How your diet can help – Throughout pregnancy and also while you are breastfeeding, you should increase your dietary intake of iron and vitamin C. Vitamin C helps in the absorption of iron from food, whereas too much tannin (found in tea and coffee) or phytate in wheat bran can reduce it. Even if you have been prescribed iron tablets, it is still important to eat iron-rich foods because the iron in food is more easily absorbed and used by the body than that in tablets. Very good sources of iron include red meat, oily fish, fortified breakfast cereals

and drinking powders such as malted milk drink, wheatgerm, sunflower seeds, raisins, rolled oats, mussels and pulses.

CONSTIPATION

This is the infrequent or difficult passing of hard, dry faeces. This condition is very common during pregnancy because the hormones soften muscles and ligaments, so the muscles of the intestines relax and, as a result, cannot move the food through as quickly as usual. As pregnancy progresses the uterus gets bigger, which puts pressure on the bowel, making it work less effectively. Iron tablets, prescribed for anaemia, can also cause constipation, so check with your doctor if you are taking them and are suffering from constipation.

Although constipation can become increasingly uncomfortable (and can lead to haemorrhoids or piles), it can be alleviated by making some simple changes to your diet. However, if it becomes a serious problem, visit your doctor.

* How your diet can help – Make sure that you eat lots of fibre-rich foods such as wholemeal bread, cereals, jacket potatoes and plenty of fruit and vegetables, as these will aid the movement of food though your digestive system by improving its mobility. Such high-fibre foods absorb a lot of fluid from the gut (like a sponge soaking up water), so you will also need to increase your fluid intake. Make sure you drink an extra 6–8 glasses of fluids per day and avoid caffeinated drinks such as coffee, tea and coke. Instead drink water, sugar-free squash, diluted fruit juices (prune juice is especially good at increasing the bowel's mobility), mineral and tonic water, herbal teas and milk- or yoghurt-based drinks. Regular activity such as walking, swimming and gentle stretching can also help.

Laxatives should only be used in pregnancy if advised by your doctor, because they may have side effects that could affect your unborn baby. Fybogel and lactulose are natural alternatives.

GESTATIONAL OR PREGNANCY DIABETES

Consistently high blood glucose (sugar) levels during pregnancy is known as gestational diabetes. It occurs in 2–6 percent of all pregnancies, and is most common in obese women. This type of diabetes usually disappears once the pregnancy is over, but the mother will have a higher risk of developing diabetes as a long-term condition.

The hormones produced by your placenta raises your blood sugar levels. Therefore, you need to produce more insulin to lower your blood sugar – if this doesn't happen quickly enough, then the sugar levels remain high. This sugar will then cross the placenta and reach your baby. In turn, your baby's body will respond by producing more insulin. The insulin lowers the baby's blood sugar by converting it to fat for storage, and so the baby will become larger, making delivery more difficult. A lot of fluid can also build up around the baby, causing premature labour. After delivery the baby's blood sugar can drop rapidly and cause breathing difficulties and hypothermia.

Gestational diabetes can be picked up from the routine urine tests that are done at antenatal appointments. If there is sugar in your urine, you will probably have a blood test first thing in the morning (after an overnight fast) to check your blood sugar levels before you have eaten anything. Sometimes this blood test is routinely carried out at around 28 weeks. If the blood test shows that your sugar levels are high, a glucose tolerance test, which involves drinking a sugary solution and seeing how high your blood levels rise during the next two hours, may be necessary. If your sugars are high, this confirms you have gestational diabetes and your doctor will advise you on treatment, which normally centres around dietary changes. It is usually best to see a dietitian who can recommend the types and amounts of food that you need.

* How your diet can help – If your blood sugar levels are high, you may need to monitor your own blood sugar levels throughout the day and modify your diet by cutting out sugary foods and drinks such as jam, honey, puddings, sweets and squash. You should also increase your intake of carbohydrate foods that are slowly digested and have a low glycaemic index or low blood sugar effect, such as wholegrain bread, pasta, basmati rice and rolled oats (muesli or porridge). Eating more fruit and vegetables can help control blood sugar levels too, as the sugar is broken down and absorbed more slowly into the bloodstream (see also page 36).

Most women are able to control their blood sugar levels with diet and exercise, but if this doesn't work, then your doctor may prescribe medications.

HEARTBURN

Heartburn is a specific type of indigestion during which the acid from the stomach leaks back up into the gullet and causes a painful burning feeling in the chest. This condition is very common and affects around two thirds of pregnant women. It caused by the pregnancy hormones, which relax the valve at the entrance to the stomach, making it difficult for it to close properly and therefore allowing stomach acid to escape. The problem tends to get worse as the uterus gets bigger and puts pressure on the stomach. Although it is most common in the last three months of pregnancy, some women experience it as early as 20 weeks. However it does disappear after the birth.

Adjusting your diet, sitting posture and sleeping position can help alleviate this condition. However, if it begins to severely affect your eating or is causing a great deal of pain, visit your doctor.

* How your diet can help – Eat frequently, as many as six small meals a day, rather than two or three large ones, as this will mean that there is less pressure on your stomach. Try to identify which foods and drinks give you heartburn, but generally avoid rich, fatty, spicy or very acidic foods like pastries, curries and some citrus fruits as they often make it worse. Eat starchy foods and non-acidic fruit and vegetables to help your digestion. Low-fat dairy foods, cereal products and lean meats are useful foods for this condition too. Don't eat just before you go to bed and avoid bending or exercising just after eating.

You should also avoid strong tea, coffee and very acidic drinks. You may find that milk or fizzy water helps to alleviate your symptoms. Raw garlic may also help. Avoid over-the-counter remedies – consult your doctor about suitable medications.

MORNING SICKNESS OR NAUSEA

This is one of the most common complaints of pregnancy, affecting around 70–80 percent of all pregnant women. It can actually occur at any time of the day, and symptoms can vary from mild nausea to persistent vomiting. It can begin as early as a few days after you have missed your period and usually trails off some time between the third and fourth month of pregnancy. Morning sickness is attributed to a number of factors, including hormonal changes, changes in blood pressure and changes in your digestive system (which slows down in order to absorb more nutrients). Tiredness and dehydration can make it worse, but be reassured that, although it can make you feel wretched, it won't harm your baby.

* How your diet can help – There is no guaranteed cure for morning sickness, but there are a few dietary changes that can help. For example, often the very sight and smell of certain foods can make you sick, but nausea is always worse when you are hungry. Try eating a slice of bread or a couple of dried crackers or biscuits such as arrowroot or ginger

nuts first thing in the morning or in between meals to stop getting hungry. Snacks such as dried fruit, bananas and cereals are also handy to have on hand to help stave off hunger pangs. Remember, too, that bland foods such as rice, potatoes, bread and cereals are often easier to keep down.

Your sense of smell will probably become quite acute during pregnancy. Many women find the smell of food off-putting at this time, so avoid strong smells. Try eating your food cold so that you don't have to smell the food as it cooks. Sandwiches and salads, for example, can be just as nutritious as a cooked meal. If you want something hot, then try making quick snacks, such as beans on toast. Alternatively, ask someone to prepare meals regularly while you are pregnant.

You should also ensure that you drink plenty of fluids, especially if you are actually vomiting, as you need to replace lost fluid to prevent dehydration. Drink water, milk and well-diluted non-acidic fruit juices and avoid caffeinated drinks. You should also make sure that you take the drinks in small amounts, but regularly, so that you don't get over full. You can increase your fluid intake from fruits, like melons, as well as soups, custards and yoghurt too.

Some specific nutrients and foods may help. For example, some studies have shown foods rich in zinc, such as pumpkin

seeds, or rich in B6, such as broccoli and ginger, can help. Ginger in particular is often advised for morning sickness (but not in large doses).

WEIGHT GAIN PROBLEMS

An acceptable healthy weight gain during pregnancy is between 11–15kg (25–35lb), though on average most women put on between 9.5–13.5kg (20–30lb). It is usual to gain around 10 percent of your total pregnancy weight in the first three months, at least half of it in the middle few months and around 4kg (9lb) in the last three months – although this can vary for some women.

Your weight gain will depend on your pre-pregnancy weight, your metabolism and your level of activity during your pregnancy. If you started off overweight or underweight (above 100kg/220lb or less than 50kg/110lb, depending on your height and build) then you may need specialist advice. Although the range of weight gain is great, there are disadvantages to being at the outer limits of it.

Weight gain can cause a great deal of anxiety for the expectant mother and also carries health risks. Gaining a lot of weight makes you more likely to develop varicose veins, breathlessness, heartburn, swelling and increases your risk of developing complications such as high blood pressure, pregnancy-related diabetes or pre-eclampsia (pregnancy induced high blood pressure and toxaemia). Therefore it is important for overweight women to seek expert dietary advice .

Alternatively, if you haven't gained enough weight, this may affect your own health and the baby's birth weight as low weight gain tends to be associated with lower birth-weight babies. However, if you are in good health, eat healthily and aren't smoking, simply eating more will not increase the weight of your baby, as birth weight depends on other facts (see chart).
∗ How your diet can help – Although you should be focusing on getting the right balance of nutrients for two bodies, you don't need to double the quantity of food that you eat. Pregnancy is therefore definitely not a time for gorging yourself. Conversely, it is also not the time to be dieting. Calorie-dense foods like sweets and chocolate, though tempting, only provide you with empty calories – the weight gain without the nutritional benefits. So keep them to a minimum – for treats and special occasions (like labour).

Both you and your baby need to be well nourished, so concentrate on eating a varied and balanced diet. If you have a pre-existing weight problem, then ask your midwife or doctor to refer you to a registered dietitian for specific dietary advice and expert counselling. And always alert your doctor if you are worried about your weight gain or lack of it.

WHERE THE EXTRA WEIGHT GOES	
THE BABY	Average birth weight 3.2–3.5 kg (7–7½lb). This can vary depending on your genes, own birth weight, physical size, number of previous pregnancies, age, ethnic origin, health status and diet.
INCREASED BLOOD SUPPLY	1.25l (2¼ pints) – this is about 2 kg (just over 4 lb)
AMNIOTIC FLUID	Around 1kg (just over 2lb)
ENLARGED UTERUS	About 1kg
PLACENTA	About 1kg
BREASTS	Just under 1kg

The remainder is laid down as extra adipose (fat) tissue for energy stores after the birth in preparation for breastfeeding, which can use up an extra 500 kcals per day, and fluid in tissues – averaging 3–4 kg (about half a stone).

grains, cereals, nuts and seeds

Rich sources of complex carbohydrates, grains and cereals also contain vitamins, minerals and fibre. Nuts and seeds are good sources of protein, vitamins, minerals and essential fats.

* **Cereals and grains** are versatile and can be used to make an enormous range of foods including bread, pasta, pancakes and cakes. You should include six to eight portions each day, as they provide plenty of energy needed for a healthy pregnancy and developing baby. Grains are a useful source of non-animal protein, are an excellent source of carbohydrate and also contain B vitamins, folic acid and fibre. Wholegrain cereal products, such as brown rice, unprocessed oats and grainy breads offer more fibre and B vitamins. Many breakfast cereals are now enriched with extra vitamins and minerals to replace those that are lost during processing.

* **Rice** – especially brown and wild varieties – is a useful source of the B vitamins and also contains calcium, carbohydrate (starch), some protein fibre and a variety of minerals.

* **Bread** is low in fat and calories, while providing plenty of carbohydrate energy (high in starch and filling). Wholegrain and granary types are more filling and richer in fibre – four slices a day will give you half your daily recommended fibre intake. All types of bread provide B vitamins, including folic acid, as well as fibre and some vitamin E. Wholemeal and wholegrain breads also provide some iron.

* **Pasta and noodles** are excellent sources of slow-release carbohydrates. They are also low in fat and calories and are useful sources of protein, which is needed to grow all the organs and tissues in your developing baby.

* **Nuts and seeds** are good sources of protein, minerals and vitamins E and B, but can be high in calories. Walnuts, brazil nuts and linseeds (flaxseeds) are rich sources of omega-3 essential fats, which cannot be made in the body. Seeds, such as sunflower, sesame and pumpkin, are good sources of fibre, minerals and polyunsaturated fats and mineral oils. Flaxseeds are a particularly nutritious option and can easily be sprinkled over breakfast cereals, salads or yoghurts to give a boost to your intake of essential omega-3 fatty acids.

PEANUT ALLERGY ALERT

* If you or your immediate family (the baby's father or baby's siblings) suffer from asthma, eczema, hay fever or other allergies, then you should avoid peanuts and peanut products during pregnancy and breastfeeding, as they can cause a dangerous allergic reaction in some children.

wild rice

olive ciabatta

pistachios

oats

fresh tagliatelle

wholemeal flour

polenta

buckwheat noodles

long-grain brown rice

pulses or legumes

High in protein and fibre, as well as many vitamins and minerals, these foods are excellent vegetarian alternatives to meat.

* **Pulses** include cannellini, borlotti and mung beans, dahl, split peas, lentils and chickpeas. All are highly nutritious, providing a mixture of slow-release carbohydrates, protein, fibre, vitamins and minerals. They are packed full of B vitamins, iron, potassium (needed for a healthy heart and nerves, and normal blood pressure), phosphorus (needed for bone and teeth formation and energy production), magnesium (necessary for healthy muscles and nerves) and manganese (required for hormone production and bone formation).

A dish that combines pulses with grains will give you complete protein, containing all the amino acids you need (particularly important for vegetarians). The soluble fibre in all types of pulses can also help to prevent constipation and keep blood sugar stable (see box below).

Canned varieties are also nutritious and have the added benefit of being quick and easy to use. However, their sodium content may be higher than that of fresh beans, so look for no added salt varieties. Remember that if you are using the dried type, you must soak and cook them thoroughly. Dried beans, in particular red kidney beans, contain a natural toxin, which is safely destroyed by cooking.

* **Soya** beans are among the few plant sources of complete protein, containing all the amino acids that make up protein. Soya products such as tofu, tempeh, soya beans, soya mince and flour can be used in soups, casseroles, stir fries and breads. Soya products are a nutritious addition to your diet – they provide vitamins, minerals and essential fats. Soya beans are particularly rich in omega-3 essential fatty acids, which offer many health benefits and tend to be limited in typical diets. Soya beans also provide a valuable amount of fibre, many vitamins and minerals and the cancer-protecting compound, genistein.

FOCUS ON FIBRE

* Fibre is essential for the gut to work effectively. When pregnant, you may find that your digestion becomes slower, making you more prone to constipation and other problems. There are different types of fibre, but the soluble fibre found in beans and lentils can help to relieve constipation a little, as well as controlling blood sugar and cholesterol. Try serving them with natural 'live' or 'bio' yoghurts to further improve the health of your gastrointestinal tract.

butter beans

yellow split peas

soya beans

tempeh

puy lentils

tofu

borlotti beans

haricot beans

black eye beans

meat, poultry and eggs

Meat and poultry are excellent sources of top-quality protein, iron and zinc. Eggs also contain complete protein and are packed with many vitamins and minerals.

* **Meat and poultry** are particularly good sources of protein because their amino acids content is similar to that needed by our bodies. Plant foods contain incomplete protein, which means they don't have all the amino acids needed by the human body, although this can be overcome by mixing them together or with dairy products. Choose the leanest cuts of meat and poultry, without skin, to reduce your intake of saturated fat.

Although you require 6g (¼oz) more protein each day when you are pregnant, you still only need to eat two to three portions of protein-rich foods each day. Meats such as beef, lamb, kidney and dark chicken meat are good sources of protein and well-absorbed iron. Liver and liver products should be avoided while you are pregnant, as they contain high amounts of vitamin A, which, in excess, is harmful to your baby (see pages 9–10).

* **Eggs** are highly nutritious because they are full of vitamins and minerals, including A, D, E, the B vitamins, calcium and iron. Many women avoid eggs because they believe that they are high in fat and calories, but in reality there are just 70kcal in a medium-sized egg. They are also an excellent source of top-quality protein for non-meat eaters.

Eggs can be used in many recipes and make a quick, nutrient-dense snack. This is especially helpful during the times when you need to eat small meals at the beginning and end of your pregnancy. Always ensure that eggs are cooked thoroughly before eating. Avoid products products containing raw egg such as fresh mayonnaise and sauces (see pages 20–1).

FOCUS ON IRON

* You need more iron during pregnancy both for your developing baby and to increase your own blood supply. When pregnant, your baby is given first priority by your body, so your own stores of iron will become depleted if you don't eat enough iron. Many women have relatively low iron stores and are prescribed iron supplements when they become pregnant. However, iron supplements can interfere with the absorption of other nutrients from your food and may induce constipation. Iron is absorbed much more effectively from food than supplements, and the presence of vitamin C-containing foods will help your body absorb more of the iron you consume. Therefore, try to include vitamin C-rich foods with every meal, especially if you do not eat meat. Fruit juice, green or red vegetables and most fruit contain vitamin C (see page 40).

hen's eggs

lamb

duck

chicken

fish

All types of fish are nutritious and low in calories. They are good sources of high-quality protein, vitamin B12 and important minerals, such as iodine and selenium.

Fish is a good choice for lunch or dinner while you are pregnant, as it can be cooked quickly and is full of nutrients. Whether you use frozen, canned or fresh, a small portion of fish (100g/4oz) actually contains half of the recommended daily protein requirement. Protein is needed on the body for the growth and repair of muscles, bones, hair and organs, and the production of hormones and antibodies. Protein is also required to make the extra blood cells that are needed in pregnancy.

* **Non-oily fish** such as sea bass, cod, haddock, monkfish, plaice, whiting, brim, flathead and sole are low in fat and calories. This makes them easier to digest, if you are suffering from digestive problems. They also contain iron, selenium and other essential nutrients. Cod is still the most popular white fish but others such as whiting and haddock are just as nutritious and high in protein.

* **Oily fish** includes mackerel, sardines, tuna and salmon. They are rich in essential omega-3 fats, which can help control blood pressure and are vital for the normal development of the baby. Even though they are called oily, they are still relatively lean. Buy canned fish in spring water or soy bean oil to guarantee omega-3.

Ensure that all fish is well cooked before being eaten, in order to prevent infection from the bacteria that can grow on them and protect you from the potential risk of food poisoning. This is most important with oysters and shelled seafood such as prawns, mussels and crabs. Pregnant women should also avoid food preserved in nitrates, including smoked fish and caviar.

Cod liver oil supplements should not be taken by pregnant women, to avoid overdosing on vitamin A (see pages 9–10). Instead, include oily fish at least twice a week in your diet.

FOCUS ON OMEGA-3 FATS

* Omega-3 fats are called essential fats because they can't be made in the body. It is important to eat them regularly, because they offer many health benefits – aiding growth, skin production and protecting the immune system. Omega-3 fats are also needed for the development of your baby's eyes and brain throughout pregnancy and while you are breastfeeding.

* A 100g (4oz) portion of oily fish such as herring, tuna or salmon each day will provide you with a significant amount of omega-3. If you don't like eating fish every day, you can get excellent amounts of omega-3 by eating linseeds, dark green vegetables and walnuts.

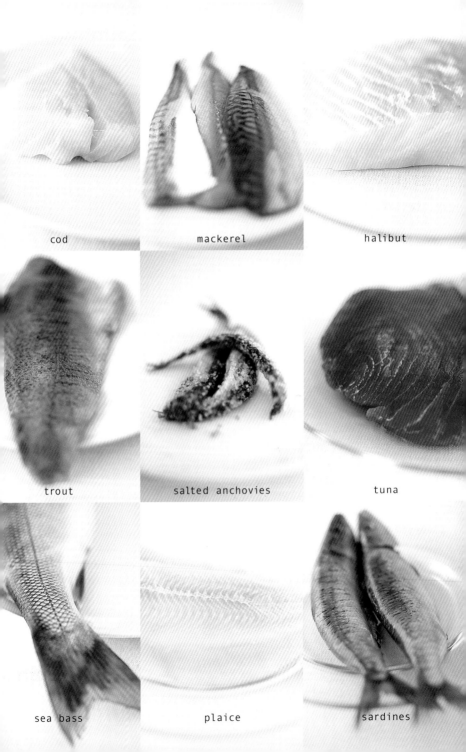

cod

mackerel

halibut

trout

salted anchovies

tuna

sea bass

plaice

sardines

starchy vegetables

These vegetables are packed full of important vitamins, minerals, antioxidants and fibre. They also provide plenty of carbohydrate energy.

Starchy vegetables provide high levels of potassium, beta-carotene and the B vitamins, including folate. Although fresh vegetables contain the most vitamin C, tinned sweetcorn, frozen peas and beans are good sources too, so don't omit them from your diet. Brightly coloured vegetables such as carrots, sweetcorn, sweet potatoes and beetroot are good sources of healthy plant chemicals, such as beta-carotene and antioxidants.

* **Carrots** are a rich source of beta-carotene, which is an antioxidant and can also be used to make vitamin A in the body.

* **Potatoes**, including sweet potatoes, are a useful source of vitamin C, starch, fibre and potassium. Potatoes contain some B vitamins and provide plenty of carbohydrate energy, which helps to satisfy hunger.

* **Pumpkins, yellow squash and sweet potatoes** are rich in beta-carotene and potassium. There are many varieties and they are easy to digest, which makes them particularly useful later on in pregnancy when indigestion can become a real problem. Pumpkin seeds contain some iron, zinc and other vital minerals, so try them as a healthy snack or add them to bread and soups.

Cooking destroys vitamin C and folic acid, so vegetables are best eaten raw or lightly cooked – try steaming, stir frying or microwaving them and make sure that they remain crisp. As they can also help to keep your blood sugar levels stable, you should try snacking on raw vegetables, such as raw carrots or peas, throughout the whole of your pregnancy rather than potato crisps, whenever you feel that you need an energy boost.

FOCUS ON ORGANIC VEGETABLES

* Organic vegetables are free from pesticides, additives and artificial growth hormones and are now widely available in supermarkets, markets, farm shops and by mail order. They have the appeal of being 'natural', but may not be any more nutritious than non-organic varieties, although they may arguably be more flavoursome. There is also no evidence to suggest that non-organic vegetables are harmful in pregnancy. However it may be preferable to buy organic if you are going to eat raw or unpeeled vegetables. It is particularly important to buy these vegetables as fresh as possible and use them straight away as they are prone to spoil quickly.

pumpkin

sweet potato

new potatoes

carrots

herbs, green leafy and salad vegetables

Leafy and salad vegetables and herbs are low in fat and calories, but packed full of vitamins, minerals, antioxidants and fibre. They provide many health benefits.

* **Dark green, leafy fresh vegetables** such as Asian greens, spinach, swiss chard and green salad leaves, such as watercress and rocket, are rich sources of vitamins, including folic acid and vitamin C. They are high in fibre (to help with constipation and digestive problems), low in calories and fat (to help maintain a healthy weight) and rich in antioxidants. Most importantly, these vegetables are high in folic acid (which is needed for the normal development of your baby's brain and spinal cord).

* **Tomatoes** and other brightly coloured vegetables, such as radish, beetroot and peppers (capsicum), are rich sources of beta-carotene and other antioxidants, both of which help to protect your baby's developing body. As with all vegetables, they are low in calories and provide healthy amounts of vitamin C, fibre and potassium.

* **Garlic** has natural antiviral and antibacterial properties. These are both excellent for protecting against infection, to which you are more vulnerable – especially in the first trimester. The regular consumption of garlic is claimed to have a number of beneficial effects, including a reduction in blood pressure and blood clots, which may be useful during pregnancy when blood pressure can increase and good blood flow is needed.

* **Herbs** such as mint, fennel and ginger roots can help to alleviate nausea and vomiting. Add them to salads and stir fries. Parsley is a rich source of vitamin C and iron. Avoid raspberry leaves and penny royal in early pregnancy as they may stimulate the uterus to contract. Although all herbal teas are seen as healthy, you should avoid the above herbs in such form while pregnant, as well as chamomile, sassafras, feverfew, foxglove, comfrey.

FOCUS ON VEGETABLES

* Many fresh salad vegetables are good sources of vitamin C, which is vital for the production of collagen – a protein required for the skin, bone, gum and teeth, and for a healthy immune system.

* Cooking destroys vitamin C and folic acid, so most vegetables are best eaten raw or very lightly cooked. Add fresh salad vegetables to sandwiches and have side salads.

* Nibbling raw vegetables throughout the day is an ideal way to keep your hunger at bay and your weight under control.

green beans

garlic

watercress

low pepper (capsicum)

purple sprouting broccoli

swiss chard

baby savoy cabbage

ginger

flat leaf parsley

fruit

Fresh fruit is a rich source of antioxidants and potassium and has the added benefit of being low in fat and calories. Aim for at least two to three servings a day.

Fruit is particularly good for pregnant women because it provides a tasty, nutritious snack between meals. Try the following – citrus fruits, apples, mangoes, nectarine, figs and also dried fruit, fruit juices and purées.

As with vegetables, cooking, storing and chopping fruit destroys some of the vitamins, so fruit is usually best eaten raw or lightly cooked. Eating fruit with its skin will give you more fibre and nutrients, but always wash the skin first to remove any pesticide residues.

Although fresh fruit is the best source of vitamin C, tinned pineapple, dried apricots and mangoes and freshly squeezed juices are good too. Brightly coloured fruits such as apricots, melons and berries provide good amounts of antioxidants and vitamin A, while fresh orange and grapefruit juice are rich in folic acid, which is essential for the normal development of your baby in the first trimester of your pregnancy.

* **Bananas** are a good source of carbohydrate energy, potassium and some B vitamins and fibre, which makes them a nutritious and filling snack. It's a fallacy that they are fattening, unless eaten in excess, as an average banana contains a similar amount of calories to most other fruits. Bananas and yoghurt are great snacks, light but sustaining.

* **Cranberries** have a natural anti-bacterial substance that has been found to be helpful in easing urinary tract infections such as cystitis, which you may be more prone to during pregnancy. They are also a rich source of vitamin C and other antioxidants. You can buy cranberry juices, sauces and fresh or frozen cranberries, which make delicious jellies, sauces (both savoury and sweet) as well as toppings for yoghurt and breakfast cereals. In fact, all types of berries and currants, fresh or frozen, are good sources of vitamin C and other antioxidants and have many health benefits.

FOCUS ON VITAMIN C

* Also known as ascorbic acid, this vitamin is needed for a healthy immune system and the formation of connective tissue, such as collagen, necessary for the formation of healthy skin, bones, cartilage and teeth. It also helps your body to absorb iron. Because it cannot be stored in the body, make sure that you eat foods that contain high amounts of vitamin C, such as citrus fruits, kiwi fruit, guava, mango, apricots and berries.

bananas

figs

grapefruit

cranberries

oranges

blackcurrants

nectarines

pineapple

mango

dairy products and alternatives

Dairy products provide valuable amounts of easily digested protein and many vitamins and minerals, particularly vitamins A, D and B2, calcium and phosphorous.

Calcium is a vital component of bones, teeth and cell structures and is needed for the normal functioning of nerves and muscles. It is also important in the blood, where it assists blood clotting, which is particularly essential for you at this time as it will prevent excessive loss of blood during and after delivery. During pregnancy, you need an extra 300mg of calcium a day to form the baby's bones and teeth, as well as protect your own, and make more blood cells. The following foods contain calcium:

* **Milk** – half a pint of milk provides a full 300mg of calcium. Skimmed and semi-skimmed varieties have less fat, but more calcium and protein than full-fat milk. Avoid unpasteurized cow's milk and raw goat's and sheep's milk.

* **Cheese** – 30–40g (1–1½oz) of hard cheese contains 300mg of calcium. Cream and cottage cheeses and fromage frais contain a tenth of the calcium of hard cheeses but contain less saturated fat. A combination of both cheeses in your diet can help you to get enough calcium. You should try to avoid soft, unpasteurized cheeses, such as brie and blue cheeses, when pregnant.

* **Yoghurt** – just one small carton (125g/5oz) has 300mg of calcium and also contains vitamins A, D, the B vitamins and phosphorus. Try to choose live or bio yoghurt, which contains harmless 'live' cultures of 'good' bacteria that help keep the gut and bowel healthy. Live yoghurt can also help relieve diarrhoea, wind and constipation if taken on a regular basis.

* **Soya milk** and rice milk are healthy alternatives to milk for those who cannot tolerate dairy products or want to avoid animal products. Choose soya milk that has had calcium and vitamins B12 and D added (check the packaging).

FOCUS ON CALCIUM AND VITAMIN D

* During pregnancy, absorption of dietary calcium increases naturally, but excessive intakes of tea, coffee, wheat bran and salt can interfere with its absorption, causing it to be lost from the body. Avoid adding salt or unprocessed bran to your diet and limit tea and coffee.

* Vitamin D is called the sunshine vitamin, because it can be made in our skin after being exposed to sunlight. Vitamin D is needed for the proper absorption and use of calcium. Milk and dairy products contain both calcium and vitamin D, while some products are fortified with both – check packaging of products such as margarines and breakfast cereals.

bio yoghurt

soya milk

ricotta

cottage cheese

mozzarella

fromage frais

cow's milk

parmesan cheese

strawberry milk

Provides fibre, protein, potassium and calcium.

spicy lentil soup

Prep time: 10 minutes, cooking time: 1 hour, serves 4

3 tablespoons sunflower oil
1 medium onion, chopped
1 clove garlic, chopped
½ large chilli, finely chopped
125g (4oz) sweet potato, diced
50g (2oz) green lentils
1 heaped teaspoon ground cumin
1 heaped teaspoon ground coriander

1 heaped teaspoon garam masala
1 heaped teaspoon tamarind paste
1 cinnamon stick
400g (10oz) can chopped tomatoes
1 litre (1¾ pints) water
Salt
Bio yoghurt, to serve
Chopped fresh coriander, to serve

Heat the oil in a saucepan, add the onion, garlic and chilli and cook until the onion is soft. Add the sweet potato and cook for 10 minutes, stirring. Add the lentils, cumin, coriander, garam masala, tamarind paste and cinnamon stick and cook, stirring, for one minute. Stir in the tomatoes and cook uncovered until the sauce reduces and thickens. Stir in the water, bring to boil, reduce the heat and simmer for 30–40 minutes. Season with salt. Purée about a quarter of it in a liquidizer or food processor. Season to taste. Serve with bio yoghurt and coriander.
PER SERVING: 174kcal/730kJ 6.5g protein 10g fat 17g carbohydrate 3g fibre

High in potassium, beta-carotene and carbohydrate energy.

carrot and ginger soup

Prep time: 10 minutes, cooking time: 40 minutes, serves 6

3 tablespoons olive oil
1 medium onion, finely chopped
2 cloves garlic, chopped
1 tablespoon chopped fresh ginger
1 teaspoon ground cumin
1 teaspoon ground coriander

200g (7oz) carrots, diced
200g (7oz) sweet potato, diced
750ml (1½ pints) chicken stock
Salt and fresh ground pepper
Fromage frais or sour cream, to serve
Chopped fresh mint, to serve

Heat the oil in a large saucepan, add the onions and cook over a medium heat until soft. Add the garlic, ginger and spices and cook for 1 minute. Add the carrots, sweet potatoes and cook for 5 minutes. Add the stock, bring to the boil, reduce heat and simmer for 20 minutes until the vegetables are soft. Purée the soup in a liquidizer or food processor. Season to taste with salt and pepper. Serve topped with a spoonful of fromage frais and some chopped mint.
PER SERVING: 95kcal/395kJ 1g protein 6g fat 10g carbohydrate 2g fibre

Contains carbohydrates, fibre, iron, potassium, manganese, selenium, zinc and B vitamins.

prunes stuffed with chestnuts and wrapped in bacon
Prep time: 20 minutes, cooking time: 20 minutes, makes 24

250g (8oz) stoned (pitted) prunes
200g (7oz) cooked chestnuts
225g (8oz) smoked rindless bacon

(approx 12 rashers)
2 tablespoons finely chopped fresh rosemary
Oil for cooking

Preheat your oven to Gas 6/200°C/400°F. Stuff each prune with a chestnut. Cut the bacon in half so that you have 24 pieces. Place 6 pieces on a clean work surface and stretch the bacon gently to expand in size lengthways. Sprinkle a little rosemary on each strip of bacon, place a chestnut-filled prune onto one end and roll the bacon up to enclose the prune. Then place into a lightly oiled roasting tray and bake for 20 minutes or until the bacon is crisp and golden. Allow to stand for 5 minutes before serving.

EACH PRUNE: 45kcal/191kJ 3.5g protein less than 1g fat 2g fibre

Provides monounsaturated fat, iron, calcium, minerals and B vitamins, including folate.

avocado and sesame relish with roasted garlic and yoghurt
Prep time: 20 minutes, serves 4

2 ripe avocados
1 tablespoon olive oil
3 tablespoons lemon juice
2 tablespoons tahini
1 clove garlic

1 tablespoon low-fat bio yoghurt
2 tablespoons chopped fresh tarragon
Salt and freshly ground black pepper
Brown toast, to serve

Put the avocado into a bowl and mash until smooth, add the olive oil, lemon juice, tahini and mix to combine. Smash the garlic with a pinch of salt. Add to the avocado with the yoghurt and tarragon. Season to taste with salt and pepper. Serve on brown toast or as a dip with raw vegetables.

PER SERVING: 160kcal/656kJ 3g protein 15g fat 1.5g carbohydrate 2g fibre

Has potassium, magnesium, protein and B vitamins.

Provides potassium, carotene, folate, vitamin C.

banana and pecan smoothie
Prep time: 10 minutes, serves 2

2 ripe bananas
25g (¾oz) pecans
100ml live yoghurt or soya milk
5 tablespoons fresh orange juice
Milk or water, to dilute

Place the ingredients into a food liquidizer or food processor and purée. Add milk or water to dilute to desired consistency.
PER SERVING: 221kcal/926kJ 5g protein 9g fat 31g carbohydrate 2.5g fibre

virgin mary
Prep time: 5 minutes, serves 6

1 litre (35fl oz) tomato or clamato juice
Juice of 2 lemons (approx. 6 tablespoons)
1 tablespoon Worcestershire sauce
6–12 dashes Tabasco sauce
Coarsely ground black pepper
Ice
6 thin sticks of celery

Put the tomato, lemon juice, Worcestershire and Tabasco into a jug and mix. Season, then half fill six tall glasses with ice, pour in the mixture, finish with a stick of celery.
PER SERVING 30kcal/125kJ 1.5g protein virtually fat free 6g carbohydrate 1g fibre

A refreshing way to boost vitamin C and fluid levels.

Provides energy, beta-carotene and fibre.

summer fruit juice
Prep time: 10 minutes, serves 4

150g (5oz) strawberries
125g (4oz) raspberries
1 ripe peach
5 tablespoons orange juice
Fizzy mineral water

Hull the strawberries. Peel and remove the stone from the peach. Place the ingredients into a food liquidizer/processor and purée. Add the liquid to dilute to desired consistency.
PER SERVING: 30kcal/120kJ 1g protein virtually fat free 6g carbohydrate 3g fibre 50mg vitamin C 21mcg folate

apricot and fig smoothie
Prep time: 15 minutes, serves 2

125g (4oz) dried apricots, quartered
1 piece stem ginger, roughly chopped
2 large fresh figs
3 tablespoons lemon juice
125ml (4fl oz) bio yoghurt
Milk or water, to dilute

Place the ingredients into a food liquidizer or food processor and purée. Add milk or water to dilute to desired consistency.
PER SERVING: 193kcal/820kJ 7g protein 1g fat 40g carbohydrate 6g fibre

A great source of protein, omega-3 fatty acids, potassium and B vitamins with some iron, zinc, iodine and plant antioxidants.

fish with charmoulah sauce

Prep time: 20 minutes, cooking time: 5–15 minutes, marinating time: 2 hours, serves 4

3 tablespoons chopped fresh flat leaf parsley
3 tablespoons chopped fresh coriander
2 cloves garlic, crushed with salt
1 tablespoon freshly ground cumin
1 tablespoon sweet paprika
½ teaspoon chilli flakes or ½ large red chilli, finely chopped

75ml (3 floz) extra virgin olive oil
3 tablespoons white wine vinegar or lemon juice
Salt and freshly ground black pepper
8 large sardines, boned and flattened out
(or sardine fillets) or about 1kg (2.2lb) of any
oily fish such as red mullet or sea bream

Preheat the oven to Gas 6/200°C/400°F. For the charmoulah, finely chop the herbs, garlic and spices or place in a food processor and process until smooth. Transfer to a bowl and stir in the oil, vinegar or lemon juice. Season with salt and pepper to taste. Dry the fish on kitchen towel and lay on a piece of greased foil. Season the fish with salt and pepper. If using sardines, place a spoonful of the sauce onto each fish, then place another similar-sized sardine on top of the first sardine. Season the top sardine with salt. If using a whole large fish, score the skin of the fish several times, cutting slits on both sides, down through to the bone. Spoon the charmoulah over and inside the fish. Cover and allow the fish to marinate for 2 hours or overnight in the fridge. Transfer the remaining charmoulah to a small serving dish.

Bake the fish for 5–15 minutes or until the fish is tender. Serve with the remaining charmoulah, some lightly dressed rocket and warm flat bread.

PER SERVING: 714 kcal/3000kJ 60g protein 50g fat – mainly from poly- and monounsaturated oils

This dish is very protein-rich, providing all of your daily recommended intake of this nutrient. You could easily scale down the portion sizes early on in pregnancy if your appetite is reduced or later on if your intake has diminished due to your reduced stomach capacity. The oily fish provides omega-3 oils, which are essential early on for brain, nerve and spine development in your baby.

A good source of energy with protein, folate,
calcium, magnesium, iron, zinc and beta-carotene.

pea, broad bean and pancetta pasta

Prep time: 15 minutes, cooking time: 20 minutes, serves 4

1 tablespoon extra virgin olive oil
75g (3oz) smoked pancetta, chopped
1 clove garlic, finely chopped
2 tablespoons chopped fresh marjoram
or rosemary
150g (5oz) podded peas

250g (8oz) podded broad beans
142ml (5floz) double cream
450g (1lb) fresh or dried pasta such as
pappardelle or penne
50g (2oz) freshly grated Parmesan
Salt and freshly ground pepper

Heat the oil in a heavy-based saucepan, add the pancetta and cook over a medium heat until
browned. Add the garlic, marjoram or rosemary and cook until the garlic is golden. Set aside.
Bring a saucepan of water to the boil and cook the peas and then the broad beans until soft.
Drain well. If the broad beans are large, refresh them in cold water briefly and then remove
the pale outer pod to reveal the brilliant inner pods beneath. Add the peas and broad beans
to the pancetta, stir in the cream and bring to boil, reduce the heat and simmer for 1 minute.

Cook the pasta in a large pan of salted boiling water until *al dente*, then drain well,
reserving a cup of the cooking water. Add the sauce and half the Parmesan to the pasta once
off the heat and toss to coat the pasta in the sauce. If the sauce is too thick, add some of
the reserved water to loosen it. Season with salt and pepper to taste and then serve with the
remaining Parmesan sprinkled on top.

PER SERVING: 430kcal/1800kJ 18g protein 26g fat 30g carbohydrate 5g fibre

The pancetta and Parmesan provide the animal proteins while the cream contains most of the
fat and calories. The pasta provides the complex carbohydrates and energy, making this a
balanced dish that contains a variety of all the food groups and nutrients needed for pregnancy.
You could reduce the fat by using half-fat crème fraîche.

Rich in protein, potassium, phosphorus, carotene and B vitamins, including folate and B12.

five spiced duck

Prep time: 5 minutes, cooking time: 10 minutes, marinating time: 4 hours, serves 4

4 duck breasts
100ml (3 floz) soy sauce
1 tablespoon honey
1 tablespoon coarsely chopped fresh ginger

2 cloves garlic, coarsely chopped
1 tablespoon sesame oil
1 teaspoon Chinese five spice powder
300g (9½oz) bok choy

Trim any excess fat, skin and sinew from the duck breasts and score the flesh with a large knife to form a diamond pattern. This allows the marinade to penetrate the skin. Put the soy, honey, ginger, garlic, sesame oil and five spice powder into a shallow, non-metallic dish that the duck breasts will fit snugly into and mix to combine. Add the duck breasts and turn to coat in the marinade, cover and refrigerate for 4 hours or overnight. Drain the duck breasts and pat dry. Preheat your grill to a medium heat.

   Place the duck breast skin side first into a frying pan with a heatproof handle. Cook the duck breast over a medium heat on top of the stove for 5 minutes to seal it. Transfer the pan to under the grill and cook for 5 minutes for medium rare meat, turning it once. Put the marinade into a small saucepan and bring to the boil, reduce the heat and simmer briefly, then strain it through a sieve. Blanch or steam the bok choy, drain well. Serve the sliced duck breast on a bed of bok choy drizzled with the marinade.

PER SERVING: 260kcal/1090kJ 29g protein 13g fat 6g carbohydrate 2–3g fibre 4.5mg iron

The duck gives this dish its high protein content and the bok choy its vitamin C and fibre. Duck, like other poultry, is low in saturated fat (most of the fat is in the skin) and a rich source of most of the B vitamins. Compared to chicken it has the same protein content, slightly more fat, twice as much thiamin and riboflavin and three times as much iron. It is also higher in potassium and zinc. Like chicken it can be a source of salmonella food poisoning if not cooked sufficiently, so follow the guidelines carefully and make sure you serve it hot.

Provides slow-release energy, protein, B vitamins, some folate, beta-carotene, fibre and vitamin C.

leek and anchovy pasta

Prep time: 10 minutes, cooking time: 30 minutes, serves 4

3 tablespoons olive oil
500g (1.2lb) leeks, chopped
2 cloves garlic, chopped
100g (4oz) salted anchovies
1 tablespoon chopped fresh rosemary
300–400g dried durum wheat penne pasta

150ml (5floz) double cream
Zest of 1 lemon
2 tablespoons coarsely chopped fresh
flat leaf parsley
Salt and freshly ground pepper

Heat the oil in a heavy-based pan, add the leeks and garlic and cook, stirring frequently over a low-medium heat for 20 minutes or until the leeks are soft. Rinse the salt from the anchovies or drain them of oil and coarsely chop. Remove the saucepan from the heat and stir in the anchovies, mixing them until they dissolve into the leeks (if the heat is too high the texture becomes grainy). Return the saucepan to the heat and stir in the rosemary. Set aside.

Cook the pasta in a large pan of rapidly boiling salted water until *al dente*, drain well and retain 1 cup of the cooking water. Use this to thin down the sauce if it is too thick. Add the cream, lemon and parsley to the sauce and toss with the pasta. Season with salt and pepper.

PER SERVING: 600kcal/2500kJ 18g protein 33g fat 60g carbohydrate 7g fibre

Leeks are a useful source of folate and potassium and can help the efficient functioning of the kidneys, which makes this a good dish to include in early pregnancy. They also provide useful amounts of fibre for the healthy functioning of the gut and to help alleviate constipation. The anchovies provide protein, calcium and iron as well as omega-3 fatty acids, and the parsley and the lemon boost the vitamin C content of this dish. As anchovies are high in sodium, make sure you drink more fluids to prevent yourself from becoming dehydrated. You could reduce the fat by using half-fat crème fraîche.

This dish provides protein, fibre, folate and antioxidants with some calcium.

baked fish and tomatoes and spinach

Prep time: 30 minutes, cooking time: 15 minutes, serves 4

2 tablespoons olive oil
800g (1¾lb) fresh spinach, cooked and squeezed dry
Salt and freshly ground black pepper
800g (1¾lb) trimmed fish fillets (such as salmon, monkfish, halibut, snapper), cut into 4 portions
2 tablespoons fresh marjoram or basil
2 large tomatoes or 8 cherry tomatoes, sliced
2 tablespoons crème fraîche

Preheat the oven to Gas 6/200°C/400°F. Bone and skin the fish – make sure each piece is equal so that they cook evenly. Tear 4 pieces of foil or greaseproof paper, large enough to enclose each fish fillet. Pour about ½ tablespoon of oil onto the centre of each piece of foil. Divide the spinach into four and place a portion of the spinach onto the oil. Sprinkle with salt and pepper. Place the fish onto the spinach, scatter over the marjoram or basil leaves, top the fish with four slices of tomato and ½ tablespoon of crème fraîche. Fold the foil or greaseproof paper over to enclose the fish, making sure the edges are securely sealed so that no air or juices can escape during cooking. Place the parcels onto a baking tray, bake for about 15 minutes or until the fish is tender. (The foil or greaseproof paper will balloon out once cooked, as the air inside expands.) Serve immediately with boiled new potatoes. It is a nice idea to bring the parcels to the table and allow your guests to open them up themselves.

PER SERVING: 400kcal/1660kJ 50g protein 19g fat 4g carbohydrate 5g fibre 360mg calcium 4.8mg iron 222mcg folate 30mg vitamin C

Fish is a very rich source of protein and the tomatoes and spinach provide fibre. The crème fraîche and olive oil provide most of the fat, which could be reduced if you used half-fat crème fraîche. The herbs compliment the flavours in this dish and provide some iron, vitamin C and antioxidants.

A good source of complete protein, carbohydrate energy, healthy fats and antioxidants.

fish and fennel couscous

Prep time: 30 minutes, cooking time: 15 minutes, serves 4

3 tablespoons olive oil
1 medium onion, sliced
1 large fennel bulb, halved and core removed
2 cloves garlic, sliced
1 teaspoon freshly ground coriander seeds
1 teaspoon freshly ground cumin seeds
Pinch saffron threads
Pinch ground cinnamon
½ red chilli, chopped

400g (14oz) can chopped tomatoes
Sea salt and freshly ground black pepper
600ml (1 pint) fish stock
500g (1lb 2oz) oily fish fillets (such as red mullet, sea bream), cut into large pieces
2 tablespoons chopped fresh flat leaf parsley
2 tablespoons chopped fresh coriander
300g (10oz) couscous
Harissa, to serve

Heat the oil in a large saucepan, add the onion, fennel and garlic and cook over a medium heat for 5 minutes or until the onion and fennel are soft. Add the spices and chilli and cook for 1 minute. Stir in the tomatoes and season with salt and pepper to taste, bring to boil, reduce heat and simmer uncovered for 15 minutes or until the liquid has reduced into a thick sauce. Add the fish stock and bring to the boil, reduce the heat and simmer for 10 minutes. Add the fish pieces and simmer for 5 minutes or until the fish is cooked. Stir in the herbs and allow the dish to stand for a few minutes before serving it.

Serve with steamed couscous (follow the manufacturer's instructions to cook this) and a little harissa if you like your food spicy.

PER SERVING: 660kcal/2800kJ 40g protein 50g fat – mainly monosaturates 23g carbohydrate 11g fibre

This dish is especially useful at the start of pregnancy when your baby's brain and eyes are first developing and towards the end, when your need for calories (energy) is the greatest. The fennel is particularly high in potassium and folate, and the oily fish is rich in protein, vitamin D, phosphorus, omega-3 oils and B vitamins. The couscous provides fibre and carbohydrate energy.

This dish is rich in protein, iron, manganese, selenium, zinc, potassium and B vitamins.

grilled lamb with celeriac and chestnuts

Prep time: 20 minutes, cooking time: 30 minutes, serves 4

4 tablespoons extra virgin olive oil

1 medium onion, chopped

650g (1⅓lb) celeriac, peeled and cut into 2cm (¾in) cubes

200g (6½oz) chestnuts, cooked and peeled, then coarsely chopped

2 cloves garlic, chopped

1 tablespoon chopped fresh thyme or rosemary

Salt and freshly ground pepper

75ml (6fl oz) wine or water

4 lamb chump chops

Preheat your oven to Gas 6/200°C/400°F. Heat the oil in a large saucepan, add the onion and cook over a medium heat for 5 minutes stirring frequently until the onion is soft. Add the celeriac and cook for 15 minutes or until the celeriac is lightly browned. Add the chestnuts, garlic, thyme or rosemary and season with salt and pepper to taste. Stir in the wine or water, bring to the boil, reduce the heat, cover and simmer gently for 15 minutes, stirring occasionally to prevent the vegetables from catching on the bottom of the pan.

To cook the lamb, preheat a griddle and place the chops on top until browned. Season and then place in the oven. Roast for about 5–10 minutes until cooked through, turning once during this time. Serve the celeriac with the lamb chop on the top. You can also use the celeriac mixture as a stuffing for poultry.

PER SERVING: 450kcal/1893kJ 27g protein 30g fat 20g carbohydrate 4–5g fibre

This would be an excellent choice for a main meal, both early on in pregnancy when a good iron intake is vital and later too, as iron levels often dip with the increased blood volume. The iron from the meat is better absorbed in the presence of the vitamin C provided by celeriac.

Celeriac is a tasty winter root vegetable related to celery. It has a rich flavour and starchy texture and can be eaten hot as a vegetable or sliced in salads. It is high in potassium, vitamin C and soluble fibre.

Rich in protein, manganese, selenium, zinc, vitamin C, folate and fibre.

lobster with thai style dressing and green beans
Prep time: 10 minutes, cooking time: Nil, serves 2

1 tablespoon grated fresh ginger

½ large green chilli, deseeded and sliced

1 lemongrass stalk, chopped

1 clove garlic, chopped

4 tablespoons chopped fresh coriander

3 tablespoons lime juice

2 tablespoons sunflower oil

1 tablespoon fish sauce (optional)

Salt and white pepper

2 small cooked lobsters or two large halves

8 new potatoes, boiled

175g (6oz) green beans, steamed

Put the ginger, chilli, lemongrass and garlic into a pestle and mortar or food processor and crush until you have a smooth paste. Add the coriander, lime juice, oil and fish sauce and pound or process until combined. Season with salt and pepper. Set the mixture aside until you are ready to use it. Serve it as a dipping sauce or drizzle over prepared boiled or grilled lobster with some simply prepared boiled potatoes and a green bean salad.

PER SERVING: 262kcal/1095kJ 20g protein 18g fat 5g carbohydrate 4g fibre

This is a light and refreshing dish that would be great to prepare during the last few weeks of pregnancy as a treat – especially if you are feeling bloated. The herbs and green beans included in this recipe provide most of the folate, vitamin C and fibre while the lobster is a rich source of protein and zinc.

Rich in protein, iron, fibre, potassium, phosphorus, zinc and B vitamins including B12.

pork and pistachio kebabs

Prep time: 15 minutes, cooking time: 15 minutes, makes about 16 kebabs

2 heaped teaspoons fennel seeds, freshly ground
2 cloves garlic
650g (1lb 7oz) minced pork
½ large chilli (red or green), finely

chopped   *optional*
25g (1oz) breadcrumbs
2 teaspoons allspice
50g (2oz) pistachio kernels, toasted
Salt and freshly ground black pepper

Soak 16 bamboo skewers in cold water for 10 minutes. Put the fennel and garlic into a pestle and mortar or spice grinder and grind to a smooth paste. Transfer to a large bowl. Add the pork, chilli, breadcrumbs, allspice and pistachios and mix to combine. Season with salt and pepper to taste. (You can then leave it in the fridge to marinate.)

Take a small ball of the pork mixture (about 50g/2oz) and press it around the top of a bamboo skewer so that it looks like a cross between a lollipop and a cypress tree. You need to make 16 of these and they should be approximately 10cm (4in) long. Firmly press each one so that it doesn't break up when cooking. Cook the kebabs on a preheated griddle or barbecue for 10–15 minutes or until the meat is cooked through. Serve with a mixed salad and potatoes or brown rice.

PER SERVING: 340kcal/1400kJ 36g protein 19g fat 5g carbohydrate 1g fibre

Pork is an excellent source of protein and readily absorbable iron, especially if it is served with foods containing vitamin C, such as a side salad or fruit juice. The nuts add fibre, some protein, vitamin E and essential oils. Fennel seeds also provide some nutrients and can aid digestion.

Rich in protein, zinc, iron, potassium, phosphorus, B vitamins and carbohydrate energy.

slow-cooked beef

Prep time: 20 minutes, cooking time: 2–2.5 hours, serves 4

3 tablespoons olive oil

700g (1½lb) braising beef, in 2cm (¾in) cubes

1 medium onion, sliced

30g (1¼oz) dried porcini, finely chopped, soaked in just enough hot water to cover them

2 cloves garlic, sliced

1 heaped tablespoon fresh thyme leaves

1 heaped tablespoon plain flour

500ml (18fl oz) beef stock

1 heaped tablespoon brown sugar

½ teaspoon nutmeg

1 bay leaf

Salt and pepper

Mashed sweet potatoes, to serve

Remove the soaked porcini from the hot water, then sieve the water to remove any sediment. Set both aside. Heat the oil in a casserole dish, then cook the meat in batches over a medium heat until browned. (If you add too many pieces at once they will reduce the temperature and the meat will not brown.) Remove the meat, leaving as much oil behind as possible. Reduce the temperature of the oil, add the onion, porcini and garlic and cook for 5 minutes or until the onion is soft. Add the thyme and flour and cook stirring for 1 minute. Stir in the stock, reserved mushroom water, brown sugar, nutmeg and bay leaf, mixing well to avoid lumps. Season with salt and pepper to taste. Bring to the boil, reduce the heat and simmer, covered over a low heat for 2 hours or until the meat is tender. Check after about 1 hour to make sure that the liquid is not boiling and hasn't reduced too much. Alternatively, you can preheat the oven to Gas 3/150°C/300°F and cook the beef in the oven for 2 hours.

Serve with mashed sweet potato. Traditionally, a slice of French toast smeared with mustard is placed on top of the stew just before serving.

PER SERVING: 400kcal/1700kJ 40g protein 22g fat 9g carbohydrate 4mg iron

Red meat is one of the richest sources of protein and iron. This is a good way of cooking beef and you can buy extra lean cuts if you want to reduce your fat intake.

Rich in protein, beta-carotene, potassium, fibre, B vitamins including folate, calcium, zinc, iron, magnesium and vitamin C.

poached chicken and vegetables with gado gado sauce

Prep time: 20 minutes, cooking time: 30 minutes, serves 4

Gado gado dressing
1 small onion, chopped
1 clove garlic, chopped
½ teaspoon shrimp paste (optional)
½ teaspoon chopped fresh chilli or chilli flakes
1 tablespoon sunflower oil
2 tablespoons fish sauce
125 g (4oz) coarse (crunchy) peanut butter
200ml (7oz) can light coconut milk
1 tablespoon brown sugar
25ml (1oz) water
3 tablespoons lime juice

For the salad
200g (7oz) cauliflower, cut into florets
200g (7oz) carrots, thinly sliced
200g (7oz) mangetout (snow peas)
200g (7oz) courgettes (zucchini), thinly sliced
½ cucumber, peeled, seeded and thinly sliced
1 small red pepper (capsicum), thinly sliced
1 bunch (60g/2¼oz) fresh coriander
2 poached or grilled chicken breast fillets

To make the dressing, put the onion, garlic, shrimp paste and chilli into a food processor and process until it forms a paste. Heat oil in a heavy-based saucepan and cook the paste over a medium heat for 5 minutes, stirring frequently to prevent burning. Add the fish sauce, peanut butter, coconut milk, brown sugar and water – stir to combine. Bring to the boil, reduce the heat and simmer for 20 minutes, stirring occasionally to prevent the bottom sticking. Turn off the heat and stir in the lime juice.

To make the salad, steam the cauliflower and carrots for 3 minutes. Remove them and steam the mangetout (snow peas) and courgettes (zucchini) for 1 minute. Set the vegetables aside to cool and drain. Serve the rest of the vegetables raw.

Put the steamed vegetables into a bowl, add the cucumber and pepper (capsicum) and 4 tablespoons of the peanut dressing. Toss to combine. Remove the coriander leaves from the stems and coarsely chop the stems. Add the stems and half the leaves to the vegetables. Pile the vegetables into the centre of four plates, slice the chicken and arrange it on top of the salad. Place the remaining dressing on top and sprinkle with the coriander leaves. This dish is traditionally served with caramelized onion on top.

PER SERVING: 585kcal/2430kJ 35g protein 40g fat 16g carbohydrate 7g fibre

Rich in potassium, selenium, zinc, calcium, beta-
carotene, phosphorus, magnesium, folate
and vitamin C. Also provides some omega-3 fats.

beetroot and blood orange salad
Prep time: 20 minutes, serves 4

100g brazil nuts (or walnuts)

100g (4oz) watercress, spinach and
beetroot leaves

250g (9oz) medium beetroot, cooked
and peeled

2 oranges

1 tablespoon walnut or sesame oil

1 tablespoon olive oil

1 tablespoon lemon juice or balsamic vinegar

Salt and freshly ground black pepper

Preheat an oven to Gas 4/180°C/350°F. Put the brazil nuts onto a baking tray and roast for
10 minutes. Allow to cool, then coarsely chop. Wash and spin the salad leaves, then arrange
on a large plate. Thinly slice the beetroot and pile on top of the salad. Remove the skin
and pith from the oranges and cut the segments into a bowl, pour the remaining juice into
the bowl, add the walnut oil, olive oil and lemon juice or balsamic vinegar and whisk to combine. Season with salt and pepper to taste. Drizzle the dressing over the salad and scatter the
nuts over the top. Serve immediately.

PER SERVING: 280kcal/1150kJ 6g protein 23g fat 12g carbohydrate 5g fibre

Beetroots are excellent root vegetables to include in your diet, as they are rich in potassium,
folate and vitamin C (their tops are rich in beta-carotene, calcium and iron). They are best
freshly boiled as they then contain the highest level of nutrients.

Loaded with carbohydrate energy, potassium, vitamin C, beta-carotene and folate and also provides some iron, zinc, B vitamins and magnesium.

vegetarian stuffed peppers

Prep time: 15 minutes, cooking time: 50 minutes, serves 6

4 tablespoons extra virgin olive oil
100 g (4 oz) pine nuts
1 medium onion, finely chopped
3 cloves garlic, finely chopped
1 large red chilli, finely chopped
1 teaspoon ground allspice
1 teaspoon ground cinnamon
100 g (4 oz) currants or raisins
150 g (5 oz) green beans, finely chopped
200 ml (9 fl oz) stock

Pinch saffron threads
150 g (5 oz) couscous
225 g (8 oz) ripe tomatoes, chopped
100 ml (4 fl oz) water
2 heaped tablespoons fresh oregano or parsley, coarsely chopped
Salt and freshly ground black pepper
3 large red peppers (capsicum)
3 large yellow peppers (capsicum)
1 tablespoon olive oil, plus a little extra

Preheat the oven to Gas 5/190°C/375°F. To prepare the stuffing, heat the oil in a large saucepan, add the pine nuts and onion and cook over a medium heat until the pine nuts are light golden brown and the onion is soft. Add the garlic, chilli, allspice, cinnamon, currants and green beans and stir gently for a few minutes. Season with salt and pepper to taste, and add the stock and saffron. Cook until the stock has evaporated. Add the couscous, tomatoes and water, and stir over a low heat for a couple of minutes until the couscous has doubled in size. Remove from the heat, keep stirring for a minute more then allow to cool. Stir in the chopped herbs and season to taste.

To cook the peppers (capsicum), cut a generous amount off the top of the peppers to create lids. Scoop out the seeds and membrane and discard. Divide the stuffing between the peppers, making sure the stuffing comes just over the top of each pepper. Place the lids on top. Drizzle with the remaining olive oil, then pack the peppers into a roasting tin so they fit snugly. Cook for 30–40 minutes or until the peppers are soft and the top of each is golden brown.

PER SERVING: 330 kcal/1390 kJ 6 g protein 19 g fat 30 g carbohydrate 5 g fibre 3 mg iron

Peppers (capsicum) are available all year round, making this a dish for all seasons. The red and yellow ones are sweeter, contain three times as much vitamin C as oranges and are rich sources of beta-carotene.

Provides protein, beta-carotene, calcium, iron, zinc, selenium, potassium, vitamins A and B and biotin.

pumpkin gnocchi

Prep time: 20 minutes, cooking time: 1hour, resting time: 1 hour, serves 6

700g (1½ lb) pumpkin (500g/1¼lb peeled weight)
2 tablespoons extra virgin olive oil
1 large onion
3 cloves garlic
75g (3oz) butter
1 tablespoon chopped fresh rosemary
½ teaspoon grated nutmeg
50g (2oz) freshly grated Parmesan

250g (9oz) ricotta
2 eggs, lightly beaten
100g (4oz) plain flour
Salt and freshly ground pepper
For the sauce
50ml (5fl oz) extra virgin olive oil
1 tablespoon finely chopped fresh rosemary
1 large red chilli, finely chopped
150g (2oz) freshly grated Parmesan, to serve

Preheat the oven to Gas 4/180°C/350°F. Peel the pumpkin and cut it into 1cm (⅓in) thick slices. Cover a baking tray with foil and use 2 tablespoons of the oil to grease the foil. Scatter the pumpkin over the tray and season generously with salt and pepper. Roast the pumpkin for 40 minutes or until soft. While the pumpkin is cooking, finely slice the onion and garlic. Heat the butter in a frying pan, add the onion and garlic and cook over a medium heat until the onion is soft and translucent. Add the rosemary and remove from the heat. Drain the pumpkin in a colander if watery and transfer to a large bowl, add the onion mixture and mash until the pumpkin is smooth. Set aside to cool. Add the nutmeg, Parmesan, ricotta and eggs and mix to combine. Stir in the flour at the last minute and season with salt and pepper to taste. Cover and place in the fridge for 1 hour or overnight.

Bring a large saucepan of water to the boil, add a generous pinch of salt. Roll a piece of gnocchi into a ball (about 1cm/⅓in in diameter). Add the gnocchi to the simmering water and cook until it rises to the surface. If it does not break up, it has enough flour. Dust a tray or plate with flour, then roll all the mixture into balls. Lightly dust the gnocchi with flour and refrigerate for at least 10 minutes.

To make the sauce, gently heat the oil in a saucepan, add the rosemary, chilli and salt and warm for 1 minute. Remove from the heat and allow to infuse while you cook the gnocchi in a saucepan of salted water until they rise to the surface. Remove with a slotted spoon and drain on a kitchen towel. Serve in a warmed dish with the sauce over the top, sprinkled with Parmesan.

PER SERVING: 620kcal/2620kJ 24g protein 50g fat – of which half is unsaturated 16g carbohydrate 2g fibre

High in carbohydrate, protein, fibre, B vitamins with some folate and minerals.

brown rice, lentils and spices

Prep time: 5 minutes, cooking time: 40 minutes, serves 4

100g (4oz) brown rice
100g (4oz) puy or green lentils
4 tablespoons olive oil
1 teaspoon ground cinnamon
1 teaspoon ground turmeric

1 teaspoon ground allspice
25g (1oz) butter
2 medium onions, thinly sliced
Salt and freshly ground black pepper

Rinse the rice and lentils in a fine meshed sieve and leave to drain. Gently heat 2 tablespoons of the oil in a saucepan, add the spices and cook for 1 minute. Add the rice and lentils and cook, stirring to coat the rice and lentils in the spices. Add the butter and 400ml (14fl oz) of water to the saucepan, cover and bring to the boil. Stir the butter into the rice and lentils, reduce the heat to a gentle simmer and cook the mixture with the lid on for about 40 minutes.

Meanwhile, heat the remaining 2 tablespoons of oil in a frying pan, add the onion and cook over a medium heat, stirring frequently for 20 minutes or until the onions are caramelized. Season to taste. Stir the onions through the rice and lentils, cover and allow to stand for 10 minutes before serving. The dish is delicious when served with a simply grilled or roasted piece of meat or fish.

PER SERVING: 355kcal/1484kJ 8g protein 21g fat 35g carbohydrate 3g fibre 3.5mg iron

This dish is suitable for vegetarians, as the combination of rice and lentils gives a good balance of proteins and some iron. It would also make a good snack meal if served with tomatoes and parsley, so try this early on in pregnancy if your appetite is affected by tiredness or sickness, and in the last few weeks when you need to build up your energy stores for labour.

This dish is a great carbohydrate loader, packed full of protein, iron, zinc, folate, B vitamins and fibre.

wild rice borlotti bean and bacon salad

Prep time: 10 minutes, cooking time: 20–50 minutes, serves 4

100g (4oz) borlotti beans, soaked in cold water overnight

4 cloves garlic, finely chopped

Bay leaf

3 tablespoons olive oil

100g (4oz) wild rice or half basmati and half wild rice

1 small onion, finely chopped

100g (4oz) pancetta or smoked bacon, chopped

1 tablespoon chopped fresh sage

25g (1oz) dried figs, coarsely chopped

100g (4oz) pecans, lightly toasted, or cashew nuts

Rinse and drain the beans. Put them into a large saucepan of cold water and bring to the boil. Cook, skimming any white foam from the surface. Add 2 cloves of the garlic, bay leaf and a tablespoon olive oil and cook for 45 minutes or until the beans are soft. Drain well.

Cook the rice in a large pan of lightly salted water for 40 minutes or until soft, then drain well. Heat the remaining oil in a frying pan, add the onion and pancetta and cook over a medium heat for 5 minutes or until the onion is soft and the pancetta browned. Add the sage, figs and remaining chopped cloves of garlic, then cook for 5 minutes, stirring periodically. Stir in the beans, rice and pecans, season to taste with salt and pepper. Serve hot with grilled or roasted meats or cold as a salad.

PER SERVING: 500kcal/2076kJ 14g protein 35g fat – over half of which is mono-unsaturated and polyunsaturated 5g fibre

---

As this is a cold meal, it would be a useful dish if you are suffering from morning sickness. It is also high in fibre and will help to prevent constipation. Because it is high in complex carbohydrates, it is a useful meal to help sustain blood sugar levels early on in pregnancy and provides a good source of energy for much later on too.

Rich in carbohydrate energy, fibre, potassium, beta-carotene and some iron, magnesium and calcium.

carrot and apricot kebbe

Prep time: 15 minutes, cooking time: 40 minutes, resting time: 1 hour, serves 4 – makes approximately 12 kebbe

3 tablespoons olive oil
1 medium-sized onion, chopped
250g (9 oz) carrots, cut in half lengthways and thinly sliced
250g (9 oz) sweet potatoes, thinly sliced
100g (6oz) pistachio nuts
2 cloves garlic, sliced
Salt and freshly ground pepper
75g (3oz) dried apricots
50g (2oz) raisins

3 tablespoons chopped fresh flat parsley
3 tablespoons chopped fresh mint
2 heaped tablespoons fresh breadcrumbs (approx. 2 slices)
1 egg yolk
40g (1½oz) plain flour
300ml (11 fl oz) sunflower oil, for frying
Plain flour, for dusting with
Bio yoghurt, to serve
Chopped fresh mint, to serve

Heat the olive oil in a large saucepan, add the onion and cook over a medium heat for 5 minutes or until soft. Add the carrots, sweet potatoes, nuts and garlic then season to taste and cook, covered, for 30 minutes or until the vegetables are soft and lightly caramelized. Remove the lid and cook for 10 minutes to reduce any liquid.

Put the apricots and raisins into a food processor and process until roughly chopped, or chop them by hand. Add the vegetables and pulse until roughly chopped. Transfer the mixture to a large bowl. Add the herbs, breadcrumbs, egg and flour and mix well to combine. Season with salt and pepper. Cover and refrigerate for 1 hour. Roll the mixture into balls the size of a golf ball, gently flatten them, then dust each lightly with flour. Heat the sunflower oil in a large deep frying pan, fry the kebbe in batches over a medium-high heat until golden brown on each side. Drain on kitchen towel. Serve the kebbe with yoghurt mixed with chopped mint.
PER SERVING: 580kcal/2400kJ 9g protein 38g fat – most of which is mono- or polyunsaturated 50g carbohydrate 8g fibre

The dried fruits used in this dish are excellent sources of fibre and nutrients such as iron, beta-carotene and potassium. Raisins and dried apricots make great snacks, providing quick energy boosts.

Rich in potassium, carotene, vitamin K, folate and vitamin C.

broccoli and cauliflower with ginger and mustard seeds
Prep time: 15 minutes, cooking time: 5–10 minutes, serves 4

200g (7oz) broccoli

200g (7oz) cauliflower

3 tablespoons sunflower oil

2 tablespoons mustard seeds

1 heaped tablespoon finely chopped ginger

2 cloves garlic

4 spring onions, chopped

Pinch chilli flakes or ½ large chilli, chopped

200ml (7fl oz) water

2 heaped tablespoons chopped fresh coriander

Cut the broccoli and cauliflower into small florets. Heat the oil in a large saucepan or frying pan with lid, add the mustard seeds and cook over a medium heat until the seeds start to pop, then quickly cover with the lid. Add the ginger, garlic, spring onions and chilli and cook for 1 minute. Add the broccoli and cauliflower and cook, stirring, for 1 minute, add the water and cook covered for 5 minutes or until the vegetables are just cooked. Remove the lid and cook over a high heat to evaporate any excess moisture. Add the coriander and mix to combine. Serve with steamed rice and meat or fish. The rice and lentils recipe on pages 78–9 is another good accompaniment.

PER SERVING: 120kcal/500kJ 5g protein 9g fat 4g carbohydrate 3g fibre

> This is a light, vegetarian dish that is great for early pregnancy as it contains the iron and folate needed. Many of the spices can help reduce digestive problems and alleviate morning sickness.

A great mix of fibre, phosphorus, potassium, beta-carotene, B vitamins, folate and vitamin C.

snap pea, carrot and cashew nut salad

Prep time: 20 minutes, cooking time: 5 minutes, serves 4

100g (4oz) cashews
175g (6oz) snap peas or mangetout
(snow peas)
125g (4oz) carrots
150g (5oz) red cabbage
Dressing
3 tablespoons sesame oil

2 tablespoons sunflower oil
2 tablespoons rice wine vinegar or white
wine vinegar
1 teaspoon grated or finely chopped
fresh ginger
1 tablespoon tamari or light soy sauce

Preheat your oven to Gas 6/200°C/400°F. Put the cashews on a baking tray and toast for 5 minutes or until golden brown. Allow to cool, then coarsely chop the nuts. Slice the snap peas or mangetout (snow peas) in half at an angle. Steam or microwave the snap peas for 1 minute. Remove them and leave to cool down. Next, peel the carrot into thin ribbons and finely shred the red cabbage.

To make the dressing, put the oils, vinegar, ginger and tamari or soy sauce into a salad bowl and whisk to combine. Add the vegetables and half the cashews to the dressing and toss to coat. Scatter the remaining cashews on the salad.

PER SERVING: 300kcal/1300kJ 8g protein 27g fat – most of which is mono- and polyunsaturated 11g carbohydrate 3.5g fibre

This dish is suitable for vegetarians and would be particularly good early on in pregnancy, especially if morning sickness is a problem. The carrots in this recipe provide a good dose of beta-carotene. Unless buying organic, it is best to peel carrots before using them.

Provides folate, potassium, plant antioxidants, some
B vitamins and carbohydrate.

lebanese fattoush salad

Prep time: 20 minutes, cooking time: 5 minutes, serves 4

150g (5oz) radish, sliced

150g (5oz) small tomatoes, quartered

3 spring onions, finely chopped

½ cucumber, peeled, deseeded and sliced

1 small green pepper, quartered, deseeded
and sliced

1 small cos lettuce, coarsely chopped

2 tablespoons chopped fresh flat leaf parsley,
coarsely chopped

2 tablespoons chopped fresh mint,
coarsely chopped

30g (1½oz) rocket, coarsely chopped

For the dressing

1 large clove garlic, crushed with salt

Juice of 1 large lemon

100ml (3fl oz) extra virgin olive oil

1 tablespoon sumac (optional)

Salt and freshly ground black pepper

4 pitta bread (preferably wholemeal)

Preheat oven to Gas 6/200°C/400°F. Chop the vegetables into small pieces and put them into
a bowl and mix gently to combine.

To make the dressing put the garlic, lemon juice, olive oil and sumac into a bowl and whisk
to combine, seasoning to taste with salt and pepper. Add the vegetables to the dressing and
toss to coat (this may be done up to 30 minutes in advance and left to marinate). Spread
the pitta bread out onto a baking tray and bake for 3–5 minutes or until the bread is toasted
at the edges. Break the bread into small pieces and mix through the salad with the chopped
herbs and rocket.

PER SERVING: 444kcal/1856kJ 8g protein 26g fat 46g carbohydrate 4g fibre

---

This is a useful starter during the middle months when your appetite usually increases, since
the dish is filling without being fattening. As the fat is mainly from olive oil this will increase
your intake of the essential oils and vitamins that are needed throughout pregnancy, but particularly at the beginning when your baby's brain and eyes are forming.

Contains potassium and trace elements including calcium, magnesium, phosphorus and iron, small amounts of the B vitamins and vitamin C.

poached pears

Prep time: 20 minutes, cooking time: 40 minutes, resting time: 4 hours, serves 4

4 large Conference or Comice pears, peeled
500ml (18fl oz) clear apple or pear juice
50g (2oz) unrefined caster sugar
½ vanilla pod, split down the middle
1 small cinnamon stick
1 stem preserved ginger, sliced or chopped

1 tablespoon ginger syrup (optional)
Pinch Chinese five spice
Fromage frais, to serve
Shortbread or biscotti, to serve

Put the peeled pears in a small saucepan so they fit snugly. Add the apple juice, sugar, vanilla, cinnamon, ginger, ginger syrup and five spice and bring to the boil, then reduce heat to a gentle simmer. Cover the pears with a disc of greaseproof paper and cook for 20–30 minutes or until the pears are soft. Cooking time will vary depending on how ripe the fruit is. Remove the saucepan from the heat, and turn the pears over so all sides have been coated in the liquid. Keep them covered with the greaseproof paper and allow to infuse 4 hours or overnight. Serve warm or at room temperature with fromage frais and a biscuit.

PER SERVING: 200kcal/840kJ less than 1g protein virtually fat free 30g carbohydrate 2g fibre

This light refreshing dessert is low in calories and fat, and rich in the soluble fibre pectin as well as carbohydrate. It's a light and refreshing dish to serve at any time during your pregnancy but particularly during the early weeks, when you may prefer a lighter diet and during the last few months when you can only eat small frequent meals.

Pears are a brilliant source of natural sugars, high in fibre, potassium and vitamin C and only contain 70 kcal! They are also well tolerated, which makes them ideal fruit to include in pregnancy especially when constipation, indigestion or sickness is a problem.

This recipe provides vitamins A and D, some B vitamins, iron, zinc, calcium and phosphorus.

chocolate cake

Prep time: 15 minutes, cooking time: 20–30 minutes, serves 6

200g (7oz) 70 per cent dark chocolate, broken into small pieces
100g (4oz) butter
100g (4oz) sugar
4 eggs, separated

25g (1oz) plain flour
25g (1oz) cocoa
Cocoa, for dusting
Half-fat crème fraîche, to serve

Preheat the oven to Gas 4/180°C/350°F. Lightly grease and flour a 20cm (8in) springform tin. Melt the chocolate, butter and half the sugar into a heatproof bowl over a saucepan of simmering water, making sure that the base of the bowl is not touching the water so that the chocolate does not get too hot. Whisk the egg yolks into the chocolate. Fold in the sifted flour and cocoa. Whisk the egg whites with a pinch of salt in a clean dry bowl until soft peaks form. Add the remaining sugar and whisk until combined. Fold the egg whites into the chocolate mixture. Spoon into the prepared tin. Cook for 20 minutes or until the centre is just set or firm. Allow to cool then dust with cocoa. Serve with half-fat crème fraîche.

PER SERVING: 430kcal/1805kJ 7g protein 28g fat 40g carbohydrate 2mg iron

This cake provides a useful source of calories when you are not eating well, and particularly during the last few weeks when you need extra calories for your rapidly growing baby in preparation for birth.

A good source of carbohydrate energy with some
healthy antioxidants, calcium, vitamin C and fibre.

blackcurrant mousse

Prep time: 30 minutes, setting time: 4 hours, serves 6

6 leaves gelatine (or 11g gelatine powder)
300–500g (10–16oz) blackcurrants
(500ml/18fl oz total purée measure)
100–150g (4–5oz) caster sugar, depending
on how sharp the blackcurrants are
150ml (4¾fl oz) blackcurrant syrup
250ml (9fl oz) Greek style thick yoghurt
Biscotti or a packet of butter biscuits, to serve

If using gelatine leaves, soak them in cold water until soft. Wash the blackcurrants and drain
well, then remove and discard the stems. Put the blackcurrants into a saucepan, add the sugar
and syrup and stir over a low heat until the sugar dissolves. Push the mixture through a sieve
and reserve the purée. Drain the gelatine leaves and mix with about 3 tablespoons of the
blackcurrant purée, placing in a small saucepan. Stir the mixture over a low heat until the
gelatine dissolves. Do not boil or the gelatine will not set. If you are using gelatine powder
then use 200ml (7fl oz) of the blackcurrant purée and bring it to just below boiling point.
Remove from the heat, sprinkle over the gelatine powder and mix briskly until dissolved.

   Stir 2 tablespoons of the blackcurrant purée through the yoghurt, then fold through the
remaining blackcurrant purée and the cooled gelatine mixture. Spoon the mousse into ramekins,
small bowls or glasses. Cover with cling film and refrigerate for 4 hours until set. Serve with biscotti.

PER SERVING: 140kcal/590kJ 2g protein 3g fat 23g carbohydrate 3–4g fibre

Mousses are generally low in calories and fat but high in flavour, making them the perfect end
to any meal. Most include raw eggs, which are not recommended during pregnancy, but this one
doesn't and would be a good recipe to base other fruit mousses on too. Vegetarians could use
agar instead of gelatine to set it. You could reduce the fat by using half-fat crème fraîche.

Contains some B vitamins, vitamins A and D and small amounts of most minerals.

mango and lime upside-down cake

Prep time: 20 minutes, cooking time: 40 minutes, serves 6

2 large ripe mangoes, peeled, stoned and cut into strips
2 pieces preserved stem ginger, coarsely chopped
Juice and zest of 2 limes
Sponge cake
100g (4oz) unsalted butter, softened

100g (4oz) unrefined caster sugar
2 eggs, lightly beaten at room temperature
200g (7oz) plain flour
1 teaspoon baking powder
100ml (4floz) milk
Grated or dessicated coconut, to decorate
Bio yoghurt, to serve

Preheat the oven to Gas 4/180°C/350°F. Put the mango, ginger and lime juice into a bowl and gently mix to coat the mango in the lime juice. Reserve the zest to use in the sponge cake. Grease and line a 20cm (8in) cake tin with baking paper, so that it comes slightly up the sides of the tin in order to stop juices escaping during cooking. Alternatively, use a 250g (½lb) loaf tin, which does not need to be lined.

To make the sponge cake, beat the butter, lime zest and sugar until light and creamy. Add the eggs gradually, beating well after each addition. Fold in the sifted flour and baking powder along with the milk. Do not overmix or the mixture will be heavy. Arrange the mango slices and ginger over the base of the tin. Fold the marinade juice into the sponge cake. Spoon the sponge mixture on top of the fruit. Give the tin a gentle tap to remove any air bubbles. Cook for 40 minutes or until a skewer comes out clean when inserted into the centre. Allow the cake to cool for 10 minutes in the tin before inverting onto a serving plate. Serve it warm with yoghurt.

PER SERVING: 370kcal/1545kJ 7g protein 17g fat 48g carbohydrate 2g fibre

Mangoes and limes taste wonderful together and add vitamin C, potassium and valuable fibre to this pudding dish. The milk, flour and dairy produce add calcium, fat-soluble vitamins and protein while the eggs provide further protein and some iron.

Full of carbohydrate energy, fibre, B vitamins, potassium, calcium, phosphorus and iron.

winter fruit pudding

Prep time: 30 minutes, resting time: 3 hours, serves 6

75g (3oz) dried apricots, quartered
75g (3oz) dried figs, quartered
75g (3oz) stoned prunes, cut in half
50g (2oz) stoned dates, cut in half
25g (1oz) raisins or currants
1 dessert apple, peeled, cored and cubed
1 pear, peeled, cored and cubed
1 cinnamon stick
50g (2oz) brown sugar
500ml (18fl oz) clear apple juice

250ml (9fl oz) water
1 Earl Grey or other scented tea bag
½ vanilla pod, split in half
100ml (4fl oz) pear juice
2 pieces preserved stem ginger, finely chopped
25g (1oz) whole peeled almonds
12 slices medium sliced brown bread,
crusts removed
Custard, crème fraîche or yoghurt, to serve

To make the filling, put the dried and fresh fruits into a saucepan, add the cinnamon stick, sugar, apple juice, water, tea bag, vanilla pod and pear juice. Bring to the boil, reduce the heat and simmer for 5 minutes. Remove from the heat and stir in the ginger and almonds. Leave to cool. (The longer you leave this mixture the stronger the flavours.) Remove the tea bag, cinnamon stick and vanilla pod.

To make the pudding, line a 1 litre (1¾ pint) pudding basin with cling film. Dunk one side of each slice of bread into the fruit mixture to moisten it. Place some of the bread, with their wet sides facing outwards around the inside of the bowl, making sure they are slightly overlapping. Put the fruit and the liquid into the middle of the basin and cover the surface with the rest of the bread. Cover with a small plate that fits on top of the bread and weigh that down with a few tins or a heavy object. Refrigerate for 3 hours.

To serve, gently pull the cling wrap out of the bowl a little to release the vacuum caused by weighing down the pudding. Invert the pudding on a serving plate with a lip. Serve with custard, crème fraîche or yoghurt.

PER SERVING: 355kcal/1490kJ 8g protein 4g fat 57g carbohydrate 6–10g fibre

Rich source of calcium, iron, potassium, vitamins A and D and phosphorus.

ginger and yoghurt cheesecake
Prep time: 20 minutes, resting time: 2 hours, serves 6

500g (1¼lb) live Greek yoghurt
225g (8oz) ginger nut biscuits (approx. 20)
75g (3oz) butter, melted
50g (2oz) candied fruit, finely chopped
50g (2oz) pine nuts, coarsely chopped

50g (2oz) icing sugar (depending on how sweet your tooth is)
Zest of 1 lemon
Zest of 1 orange
Ground cinnamon, to garnish

Put the yoghurt into a sieve lined with a piece of muslin or a kitchen towel, over a large bowl. This allows the liquid to drain from the yoghurt, leaving you with a thick yoghurt that is similar to cream cheese. Allow the yoghurt to drain in the refrigerator overnight, or for at least 4 hours.

Put the ginger nuts in a food processor and process into fine crumbs. Add the melted butter and mix to combine. Press the biscuit mixture over the base and up the side of a 20cm (8in) springform tin until it is about 4cm (1½in) high up the sides. Refrigerate until set – which should take about 1 hour.

Wrap the muslin or kitchen towel around the yoghurt and gently press out any remaining liquid into the bowl. Put the strained yoghurt and the remaining ingredients (reserve some nuts, candied fruit and zest to decorate the top of the cheesecake) into a clean bowl and mix thoroughly to combine. Spread the yoghurt mixture into the biscuit case and decorate with the nuts, fruit and zest. Refrigerate for 30 minutes. Dust lightly with ground cinnamon before serving.

PER SERVING: 440kcal/1848kJ 8g protein 28g fat 35g carbohydrate 1g fibre

---

The ginger and pine nuts in this recipe are good sources of iron, which is needed throughout pregnancy but especially during the middle months when you are increasing your blood volume rapidly. Ginger is also known to alleviate nausea. The dish will also provide you with the extra calcium and vitamin D needed during the latter part when your baby's bones are growing steadily.

index

First published in 2002 by Murdoch Books UK Ltd
Copyright© 2002 Murdoch Books UK Ltd

ISBN 1 85391 552 1
A catalogue record for this book is available from the British Library.

All photography by Deirdre Rooney and copyright Murdoch Books UK Ltd
except front cover top right © Katrin Thomas and p7 © Rieder Photography,
both pictures courtesy Photonica.

Project Editor: **Claire Musters**
Art Director: **Deirdre Rooney**
Managing Editor: **Anna Osborn**
Photo Librarian: **Bobbie Leah**

CEO: **Robert Oerton**
Publisher: **Catie Ziller**
Production Manager: **Lucy Byrne**
International Sales Director: **Kevin Lagden**

Colour separation by Colourscan, Singapore
Printed in Singapore by Tien Wah Press

Murdoch Books UK Ltd
Ferry House, 51–57 Lacy Road,
Putney, London, SW15 1PR
Tel: +44 (0)20 8355 1480
Fax: +44 (0)20 8355 1499
Murdoch Books UK Ltd is a subsidiary
of Murdoch Magazines Pty Ltd

UK Distribution
Macmillan Distribution Ltd
Houndsmills, Brunell Road,
Basingstoke, Hampshire, RG1 6XS
Tel: +44 (0)1256 302 707
Fax: +44 (0)1256 351 437
http://www.macmillan-mdl.co.uk

Murdoch Books®
GPO Box 1203, Sydney,
NSW 1045, Australia
Tel: +61 (0)2 8220 2000
Fax: +61 (0)2 8220 2020
Murdoch Books® is a trademark
of Murdoch Magazines Pty Ltd